Table of Contents

Lesson 1   Finding Main Idea 4

Lesson 2   Recalling Facts and Details 14

Lesson 3   Understanding Sequence 24

Lesson 4   Recognizing Cause and Effect 34

Lesson 5   Comparing and Contrasting 44

Lesson 6   Making Predictions 54

Lesson 7   Finding Word Meaning in Context 64

Lesson 8   Drawing Conclusions and Making Inferences 74

Lesson 9   Distinguishing Between Fact and Opinion 84

Lesson 10   Identifying Author's Purpose 94

Lesson 11   Interpreting Figurative Language 104

Lesson 12   Summarizing 114

Review 1–12 124

Finding Main Idea

Learn About Finding Main Idea

Thinking about the strategy

The key to understanding written information is to think about how facts and ideas are organized. What are the most important points that the author makes? How does one point lead to the next?

When you read paragraphs of information, look for the author's organization. Suppose that you are reading an article about careers in plant science, or botany. You come to the heading "Where Botanists Work." The paragraphs under that heading give information about that topic. The **main idea** is the most important idea about the topic. A main idea can be stated as a sentence; for example: *Botanists work in varied settings.* Information about the varied settings—where each setting is, what work is done there—are details that support the main idea.

Sometimes you can find the main idea stated in the first or last sentence of a paragraph. Often, the main idea is not directly stated. You can figure out the main idea by noting the topic, thinking about the details of information, and deciding what important idea they support.

Studying a model

Read the passage and the notes beside it.

Topic: Botany

Main Idea: stated in first sentence

Supporting Details: kinds of work botanists do

Botany, the scientific study of plants, is a broad category in which there are many specialties and kinds of work. Major global concerns—how to produce food, how to protect the environment—are also the concerns of botanists. Some botanists spend most of their time in laboratories, studying the chemical products and characteristics of plants. Other botanists may focus on genetic research or on plant breeding projects. Botanists who work on programs to protect natural resources may spend long hours at outdoor sites. Botanists also work in educational programs, responding to questions from the public about growing and managing plants.

Topic: Botanists

Main Idea: could be stated, "Botanists pursue their interests to get advanced training."

Supporting Details: future botanists' interests

educational requirements

People who become botanists often show an interest in the natural world from an early age. They notice details in living things. They ask many *why* questions. Often, they like to collect things and organize them. Future botanists enjoy outdoor activities. In high school, they are interested in math, chemistry, and biology, as well as other subjects. Botanists begin their training in college, usually by majoring in biology or chemistry. To specialize in botany, they go on to earn a master's degree and then a doctoral degree (Ph.D.) from a university.

Extensions in Reading™

BOOK 8

CURRICULUM ASSOCIATES®, Inc.

Acknowledgments

Product Development and Design by Chameleon Publishing Services
Written by Lee S. Justice
Illustrated by Leslie Alfred McGrath

Credits

Special thanks to Dr. Rafael Corral, El Paso, Texas, for the interview "Talking with Dr. Rafael Corral."

"The Columbian Exchange," "Lost for Centuries," "Hurricane!" and "WHAT? I Can't Hear You"
are reprinted with permission of Lee S. Justice. Copyright 2001.

"Heat" by H. D. Doolittle, from COLLECTED POEMS, 1912–1944, copyright ©1982
by The Estate of Hilda Doolittle. Reprinted by permission of New Directions Publishing Corp.

"The Waking," copyright 1953 by Theodore Roethke, from THE COLLECTED POEMS OF THEODORE
ROETHKE by Theodore Roethke. Used by permission of Doubleday, a division of Random House, Inc.

"Pure Rotten" by John Lutz. © 1977 by Renown Publications, Inc.

"Go with the Flow" by Sara Golland is reprinted with permission of the author. Copyright 2001.

The excerpt of the interview with Sylvia Earle is reprinted with permission of *The Boston Globe Magazine*
(as published in *The Boston Sunday Globe*), December 13, 1998; Permission conveyed through
Copyright Clearance Center, Inc.

Learn About a Graphic Organizer

*Understanding
a main idea chart*

A **main idea chart** helps you focus on the organization of information. You can make a main idea chart to take notes during and after reading.

The charts below show information from the passage on page 4. Notice how the supporting details point to a main idea.

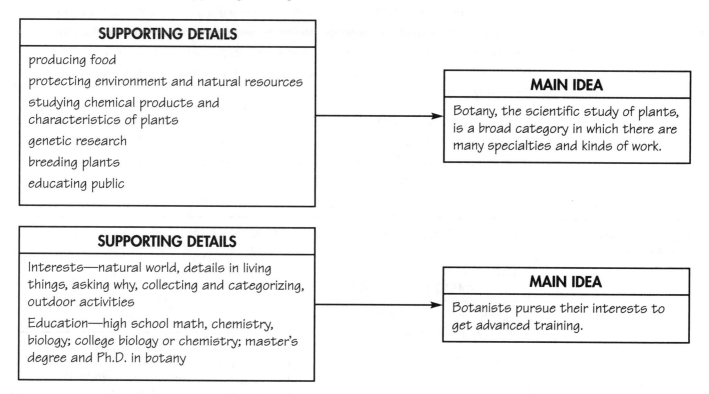

SUPPORTING DETAILS
producing food
protecting environment and natural resources
studying chemical products and characteristics of plants
genetic research
breeding plants
educating public

MAIN IDEA
Botany, the scientific study of plants, is a broad category in which there are many specialties and kinds of work.

SUPPORTING DETAILS
Interests—natural world, details in living things, asking why, collecting and categorizing, outdoor activities
Education—high school math, chemistry, biology; college biology or chemistry; master's degree and Ph.D. in botany

MAIN IDEA
Botanists pursue their interests to get advanced training.

In the samples shown, one chart is made for each paragraph. You can also find the main idea of two or more paragraphs, or of a whole section of informational writing. The supporting details in both paragraphs on page 4, for example, could point to this main idea:

MAIN IDEA
Botanists pursue their interest in the natural world, get advanced training, and work in many specialties of plant science.

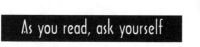

As you read, ask yourself

- What is the topic?
- What idea about the topic does the information support?

Learn About a Form of Writing

Focusing on an interview

You have probably watched or listened to **interviews**. Someone—an actor, an author, a musician, a politician, an expert—answers questions posed by a reporter. The audience hears what the person sounds like and learns about the person's work, ideas, opinions, and plans.

Interviews are spoken, but because they can be transcribed (put into print), they may also be read. Published interviews are found in newspapers, magazines, books, and in on-line sources. Although you must imagine the person's voice when you are reading an interview, you have the advantage of being able to reread and take more time to learn from the person's responses.

In a printed interview, the question (often abbreviated Q) is set off from the answer (often abbreviated A), sometimes in a different typeface. The question is like a heading in an informational article. The question will point out the topic and lead you to the main idea in the answer.

Organizing ideas in a main idea chart

A main idea chart can help you sum up the most important information in an interview.

SUPPORTING DETAILS
Facts and ideas given in answer to the interview question

→

MAIN IDEA
Summary statement of the answer to the interview question

Prepare for the Reading Selection

Gaining knowledge

The pages that follow contain an interview with Dr. Rafael Corral, a botanist and environmental biologist. The interview was recorded during a visit with Dr. Corral at his laboratory and field sites. Before reading the interview, read the following introduction.

Introduction

It is late September. The sandy West Texas landscape looks thirsty, and the air feels hot and dry. The sun shines fiercely on the blacktop parking lot next to a simple building of cinderblocks.

Inside, cool air fills a spacious, orderly room. Floor-to-ceiling cabinets line two walls, holding stacks of neatly arranged laminated sheets of pressed plants. Large worktables hold microscopes. Computers and enormous flower presses rest on cabinets. Reference books sit on shelves. Everything has its place. It is orderly here, but also busy—the phone rings continually from the office next door.

The office and the large room are the workplace of a scientist. Dr. Rafael Corral is a botanist specializing in endangered species of the Chihuahuan Desert, the largest North American desert. He is helping to build scientific understanding of desert ecosystems.

Learn Vocabulary

Understanding vocabulary

The boxed words below are **boldfaced** in the selection. Learn the meaning of each word. Then complete the sentence with the word that fits in the blank.

inventory
impale
erosion
adapted
drought
evaporation
transpiration
expand
contract
rupture

1. _____ To stretch or grow larger is to ____ .

2. _____ A liquid changes to a gas during the process of ____ .

3. _____ Soil is carried away by water during the process of ____ .

4. _____ An example of an organized ____ is a library catalog.

5. _____ To break is to ____ .

6. _____ To survive in the desert, living things have ____ to changes in temperature.

7. _____ To pin down with a sharp instrument is to ____ .

8. _____ Plants give off water through their leaves during the process of ____ .

9. _____ The supply of water is low during a ____ .

10. _____ To become narrower or smaller is to ____ .

Reading Selection—Part One

Before you read the first part of the interview "Talking with Dr. Rafael Corral," reread the introduction on page 7.

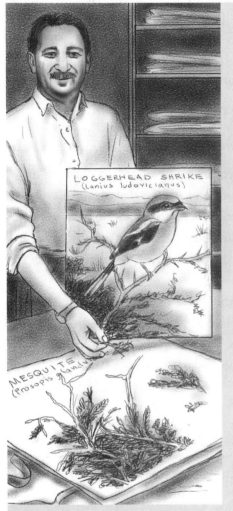

Talking with Dr. Rafael Corral

Q **What is the purpose of assembling a collection of plant specimens?**

A A collection like the one I've been working on has many uses. This is not only an **inventory** of plants for botanists but a reference collection for other associated uses. For example, scientists do bird counts or bird-identification studies. Birds eat seeds, or they eat insects that live on trees or plants. Birds use the plants for nesting, for breeding, and for cover. Some species—the birds called shrikes, for instance—even use the thorns of plants like mesquite to **impale** grasshoppers, small lizards, and other prey. The same connections apply to studies of mammals. Field scientists who are studying birds or mammals or any other animal will send me tiny pieces of plant matter—twigs, little branches, leaves, dry fruit—and I help with the identification.

Plants reveal many things. Particular plants are indicators of weathering, and of water accumulations. Special plants are found growing in soils with a high content of clay, for example, and you don't find those plants anywhere else. Having a record collection helps people working on many projects—**erosion** control, soil studies, land use, and other things.

This collection shows which native plants grow in different kinds of soils. If the population in the city grows at the current rate, there will be serious water problems for this region within the next 20 years. There's a movement toward using native plants for landscaping, because they are low-water plants. Instead of having roses, which require a lot of water or care, people can landscape with blooming plants that are native to these soils. Some have spectacular shapes.

Q **Are there any plants that grow only in this part of the world?**

A Yes, there are many plant species representative of the Chihuahuan Desert. They have **adapted** to a climate in which most of the rain falls in the summer, which is hot. Winters are mostly mild and drier. The lechuguilla (lech-uh-GEE-yuh) is a kind of agave (ah-GAH-vay) that grows only here. Its life cycle is typical of members of the agave family. The plant takes several years before it blooms and produces seeds, and then it dries and dies. But by then several underground stems have been produced, which in turn will produce new rosettes, or heads. Each flowering stalk produces hundreds of seeds as well.

lechuguilla
(Agave lechuguilla)

Q Why are desert plants interesting to you?

A They have adaptations for a very dry environment. Plants in the desert have to be able to store water and survive for long periods of **drought**, sometimes years. Sometimes their whole cycle, from seed back to seed, has to take place in just a few weeks in the wet season. Some desert plants store everything underground in big structures filled with plenty of sugars and water, so they have the food they need to grow the next year. Some plants have waxes and all kinds of protective coats on the leaves to prevent **evaporation**.

I love plants because they are the earth's producers—their food makes all life possible. The more I study desert plants, the more interested I am in them, because they have developed ways to live in very dry and hot places—places that we humans don't always see as attractive. But for these plants, not having rain is just a natural part of their cycle. If it doesn't rain this year or next year, it will rain the following year. So they wait for a better time.

Q How did you become interested in botany?

A I grew up in Mexico, and saw many uses for plants when I was a child. We tasted the sweet nectar from certain flowering plants, and we made tea out of roots, and we always ate plants. We grew corn and beans and barley and a few vegetables too. When I was in elementary school, one of our teachers told me that every plant has a name in Latin, and the name is valid everywhere. I learned a few names—for corn, beans, a few plants—and the sounds in Latin were interesting to me. We were even competing, one student versus another, about who knew more Latin.

Completing a main idea chart

Complete this main idea chart for the first question and answer in the interview.

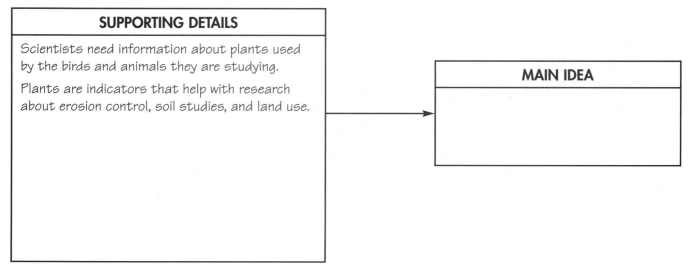

SUPPORTING DETAILS

Scientists need information about plants used by the birds and animals they are studying.

Plants are indicators that help with research about erosion control, soil studies, and land use.

MAIN IDEA

Read the second part of the interview "Talking with Dr. Rafael Corral."

Q What is unusual about the desert plants called cacti?

A Their adaptations. For example, cacti don't have any leaves—the spines are considered to be modified leaves—so they reduce the loss of water by **transpiration**. All the green tissue is in the fleshy stems. The stem design is also an adaptation. Most cacti stems can make accordion movements. The stems have pleats, also called ribs, or they have bulging parts called tubercles, or thick flat pads, or other similar designs. The design allows the stems to **expand** with water or **contract** as the water is used, according to the season. Sometimes, in the winter when it's very dry, or better yet,

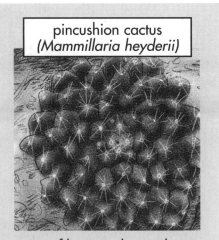

pincushion cactus
(*Mammillaria heyderii*)

in the May-June period when we haven't had rain for months, you see signs of how much cacti have contracted. For instance, when the cactus *Mammillaria heyderii* is full of water, it pushes out the soil around it. Then, as it uses up the water, there is a visible gap between the stem and the soil.

    The outer skin of cacti cannot **rupture**. They're great! They can survive many months without rain, and when the rain comes, they just absorb water and replenish the loss. They have ample resources most years, and enough water and nutrients to bloom every year regardless of drought.

Q What sites in the desert are especially valuable habitats?

A An arroyo is an area of water drainage, or a wash. It carries water during rainstorms. Because it has more water, many plants grow along an arroyo. There is room for more birds, more nesting sites, more cover, and more insects. It has greater biological diversity—that means there are many more kinds of living things here than in other desert places. An arroyo is also a sort of corridor for birds that migrate. Migrating birds fly twice a year—back and forth, north and south, summer and winter. An arroyo is a feeding area for these birds, and some of them also nest here.

Q Why should people try to protect wild plants?

A Wild plants and every animal that we find in the desert or the forest or anywhere—they all have roles. If we remove one kind of living thing here, another kind of living thing there, we make changes in the connections. Sometimes we might kill off a kind of insect without realizing that it is an important pollinator of a cactus—it helps the cactus grow seeds. When we take out the insect, the cactus can't get pollinated, and it won't produce seeds. The insect has disappeared, and so has the cactus. Then the animals that eat the cactus or the seeds have to find something else to eat. These animals will have to compete with other animals for the food that is left. So one little change can bring many changes.

    Plants are producers. That means they use the energy from sunlight, they use carbon dioxide from the air and water from the soil, and with those ingredients they can produce sugars and the first nutrients. Then come the herbivores, the insects and other animals that depend totally on plants for food. Then we have another layer—the carnivores that eat the herbivores. There can be a second layer of carnivores, such as birds of prey. If the first link in these food chains or food webs is removed, all the living things are going to have problems finding food. They could become extinct as well.

Also, wild plants have a special genetic makeup that can be incorporated into farm crops. Genes can be introduced to assist in growth or to make a better nutrition content, and so forth. So wild plants can play a role in plants that people grow for food.

Q What training did you need to become a botanist?

A After I graduated from college with an economics and engineering degree, I studied botany in graduate school in Mexico. Then I moved to El Paso for graduate school at the University of Texas. I had to take English as a second language. Sixty to seventy percent of the time I was using the dictionary, and the rest I was studying biology and botany. It was a painful couple of semesters. But I improved and just took off from there. Environmental science was becoming more popular then, so I fit right in, because my work supports studies of the environment.

Q Why is curiosity a good thing for a botanist to have?

A Curiosity gets you to ask questions. You notice things about plants, and about animals and plants together, and you ask questions about those things. Each answer to a question gives rise to two or three or many more questions. Your curiosity keeps you asking and asking and investigating and investigating. It never ends, because there are always new things to notice and ask questions about.

Using a main idea chart   In the first chart below, show supporting details and the main idea from Dr. Corral's answer to the question, "What is unusual about the desert plants called cacti?" In the second chart, show supporting details and the main idea from his answer to the question, "Why should people try to protect wild plants?"

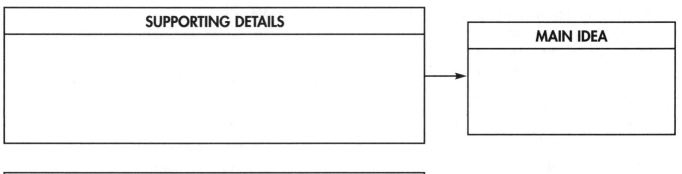

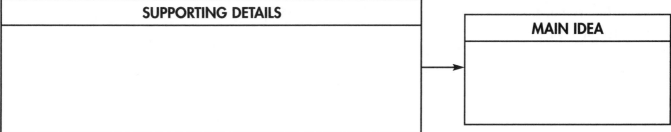

Check Your Understanding

Think about what you've read. Then answer these questions.

1. What major challenge faces all living things in the Chihuahuan Desert?
    - Ⓐ how to stay cool in the heat
    - Ⓑ how to find food
    - Ⓒ how to survive with little water
    - Ⓓ how to avoid becoming prey

2. What is Rafael Corral's inventory of plants?
    - Ⓐ a garden
    - Ⓑ a list of common and scientific names
    - Ⓒ a collection of sample parts from each plant
    - Ⓓ an organized report

3. Dr. Corral's studies support bird scientists. What question might a bird scientist ask Dr. Corral?
    - Ⓐ Does this bird eat plants or insects?
    - Ⓑ How does a plant use sunlight to produce food?
    - Ⓒ How does this bird crack open plant seeds?
    - Ⓓ What plant materials is this bird using to build its nest?

4. Rafael Corral answers the interview question, "Why are desert plants interesting to you?" What main idea does he give?
    - Ⓐ They have adaptations for a very dry environment.
    - Ⓑ They can store water for long periods, even years.
    - Ⓒ Their underground structures are filled with sugars and water.
    - Ⓓ Some plants have protective coatings on their leaves to prevent evaporation.

5. Which of these must a desert plant do in order to survive?
    - Ⓐ increase evaporation
    - Ⓑ increase transpiration
    - Ⓒ reduce evaporation
    - Ⓓ prevent weathering

6. Which of these statements about desert plants is true?
    - Ⓐ Desert plants include cacti.
    - Ⓑ Each plant of the desert is a different kind of cactus.
    - Ⓒ Only desert plants have spines or thorns.
    - Ⓓ Cacti grow only in the Chihuahuan Desert.

7. A cactus reduces the loss of water by transpiration. What does that mean?
    - Ⓐ It holds the soil firmly to prevent water runoff.
    - Ⓑ It expands during the wet season.
    - Ⓒ It has no leaves through which water vapor can be released.
    - Ⓓ It is good for landscapers because it does not need frequent watering.

8. A cactus may have tubercles. What are tubercles?
    - Ⓐ flat pads
    - Ⓑ stem bulges
    - Ⓒ ribs
    - Ⓓ pleats

9. What main idea is given about an arroyo?
    - Ⓐ Migrating birds fly along the corridor of an arroyo.
    - Ⓑ Many plants grow along an arroyo.
    - Ⓒ The plants of an arroyo provide nesting sites for birds.
    - Ⓓ It is an especially valuable habitat because of its water.

10. People might cause a cactus species to become extinct by
    - Ⓐ hunting birds of prey.
    - Ⓑ hunting the carnivores that eat the herbivores.
    - Ⓒ killing off insect pollinators.
    - Ⓓ giving a cactus plant too much water.

11. Which of these statements from the interview gives an opinion?

　Ⓐ Plants are producers.

　Ⓑ Some have spectacular shapes.

　Ⓒ Yes, there are many plant species representative of the Chihuahuan Desert.

　Ⓓ Plants in the desert have to be able to store water and survive for long periods of drought, sometimes years.

12. What important idea is Rafael Corral expressing throughout the interview?

　Ⓐ Cacti are just one group among the world's many plants.

　Ⓑ Wild plants are parts of connected systems.

　Ⓒ People should realize how attractive the desert is.

　Ⓓ The plants of the desert are in danger of dying out.

Extend Your Learning

* *Write Interview Questions*

  Write the word *botanist* as the first entry in a list of plant-related careers. Add at least nine other job titles. You may need to do research to make your list. Then choose one title, and write interview questions to ask someone who has that career. Try to write questions that will elicit full and interesting responses.

* *Make Travel Brochures*

  With other group members, find out more about the Chihuahuan Desert and the other deserts of North America. Collect maps. Find information about landforms, and plant and animal life. What national and state parks can people visit to see deserts firsthand? Make travel brochures to show pictures captioned with fascinating facts.

* *Read Another Interview*

  Find a published transcript of an interview with anyone in the news. Newspapers and magazines often publish interviews. A database of periodicals is another source. Read the interview and take notes on the main ideas.

Recalling Facts and Details

Learn About Recalling Facts and Details

Thinking about the strategy

An encyclopedia article, a textbook chapter, and a magazine article are just three examples of informational writing. They share a purpose: to inform and explain. In these informational texts and others, the title gives the general topic. The section headings show how the ideas are organized. As you read any informational text, pay attention to the title and the headings. Ask yourself questions about each heading and read to find answers.

Ask questions that begin with *who, when, where,* and *what.* The answers will be **facts and details**. Facts and details also answer *why* and *how* questions. Facts and details are the pieces of information that tell about a topic.

Studying a model

Read the passage and the notes beside it.

Questions suggested by the heading:

Who was Christopher Columbus?

When did he set sail?

Where did he set sail from?

Where was he sailing to?

Why and how did he set sail?

What was he trying to achieve?

Facts and details:

Dates, such as 1451 and August 3, 1492

People, such as Columbus, Bartolomeu Dias, and Queen Isabella of Spain

Places, such as Genoa, Italy; the Indies; the Atlantic Ocean; the coast of Spain

Things, such as trade goods from Asia and the names of the three ships

Ideas, such as European knowledge of geography

Christopher Columbus Sets Sail

Christopher Columbus, born in 1451, grew up in the great trading center of Genoa, Italy. Then he moved to another port city—Lisbon, Portugal—the center of an Atlantic Ocean trade that extended all the way from northern Europe down the coast of Africa. Columbus sailed on ships that made these voyages, and when he looked westward across the ocean, he imagined the Indies.

China and other lands of Asia were known as the Indies. Wealthy Europeans paid high prices for the spices, jewels, silks, and other treasures of the Indies. The only way that European merchants could get these items was by taking dangerous and lengthy overland routes eastward. Columbus had read the geography books of the time. It was well known that the world was round, so Columbus was sure that a ship sailing west from Europe would reach the same lands that overland travelers reached by heading east.

A voyage of exploration was enormously expensive. Columbus tried to persuade the rulers of Europe to sponsor him. The king of Portugal said no. The king chose instead to sponsor explorers such as Bartolomeu Dias, who in 1488 found a sea route to the east by sailing around the southern tip of Africa.

Queen Isabella of Spain seemed interested in Columbus's plan. But it took years for the financial arrangements to be made. Finally, Columbus had a large ship, the *Santa Maria*, and two smaller vessels, the *Niña* and the *Pinta*. On August 3, 1492, the ships set sail from the coast of Spain on a voyage west. Columbus did not know that the world was much bigger than geographers estimated, and that the Indies were not across the western ocean. Columbus did not know that his voyage would change the lives of everyone in the world.

Learn About a Graphic Organizer

Understanding an information web

When you are preparing for a test or writing a report, you will need to recall important names, dates, and other facts and details.

One way to take notes on facts and details is to draw an **information web**. A web is a useful graphic organizer for showing the connections between larger topics and related pieces of information.

This information web shows key facts and details from the passage on page 14.

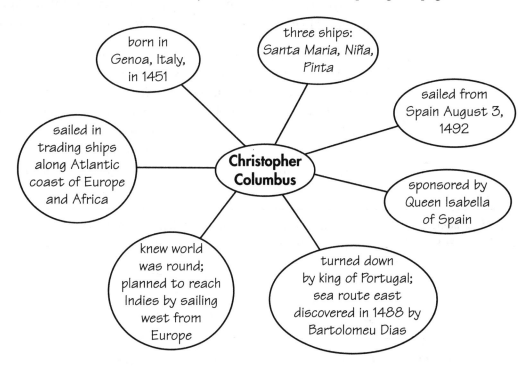

You can use the details in an information web to write a passage of your own, restating the key ideas and information. For example:

> Christopher Columbus was born in Genoa, Italy, in 1451. An experienced sailor, he tried to persuade European rulers to finance a voyage west to the Indies. The king of Portugal turned Columbus down, and instead sponsored voyages that led to the discovery of a sea route east to the Indies in 1488. Queen Isabella of Spain agreed to sponsor Columbus. On August 3, 1492, three ships set sail from Spain—the *Santa Maria*, the *Niña*, and the *Pinta*—and Columbus was on his way to changing world history.

As you read, ask yourself

- What topics are covered in the informational passage?
- What are the answers to the questions *who, when, where, what, why, how?*

Learn About a Form of Writing

Focusing on an informational article: history

An **informational article** on a topic in history presents a key period, episode, or issue of the past, and explains its importance. An author researches diaries, letters, and other first-person accounts, along with sources written by other historians. The author uses the research to tell about the events, to offer insights, and to make judgments about what "really" happened. Authors of history articles want to share their fascination with past events.

History articles show connections of all kinds. Authors may point out, for example, how a single incident or person of the past caused changes that continue to the present day. Authors often point out how two periods were alike and different.

When you read a history article, look for the author's organization of ideas. Headings can help you find topics and categories of information. For example, suppose that you are reading an article titled "The Age of Exploration," and you see this heading: "Portugal Leads the Way." Ask yourself what you expect to learn from reading the section under the heading. Example questions: *Why was Portugal so important? Who were Portuguese explorers? Where did they go? What did they achieve?* Then read to find answers to these questions and new ones. Asking and answering questions will help you focus on the key facts and details.

Organizing ideas in an information web

If you want to recall the facts and details, take notes. An information web is a useful note-taking drawing because it shows connections between topics and supporting information.

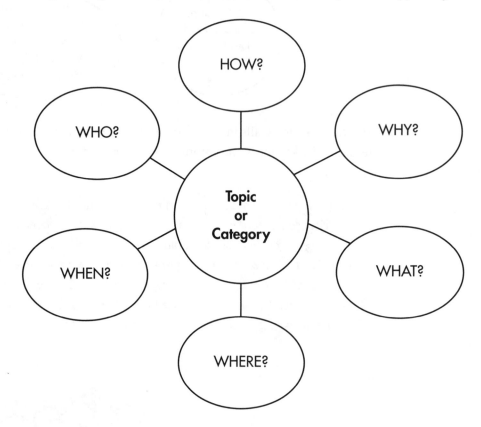

Prepare for the Reading Selection

Gaining knowledge

The pages that follow contain a history article titled "The Columbian Exchange." The adjective *Columbian* is formed from the proper noun *Columbus*, and is used to describe something related to Christopher Columbus's voyages to the Americas. Christopher Columbus completed four voyages. He traveled to Cuba and other islands of the Caribbean. He brought settlers to the island he called Española (Hispaniola—the island that is shared by the nations of Haiti and the Dominican Republic). Columbus sailed to the coast of Central America, and along the shores of South America. He returned to Spain in 1504 and died two years later, still believing that he had discovered lands off the coast of Asia. The mistaken connection with the Indies resulted in the name given to all the native peoples of the Americas: They would be known as Indians.

For more than fifty years after Columbus, the conquistadores of Spain controlled the exploration of the Americas. In search of treasure, mainly gold, they began the conquest of the great civilizations of Mexico and of Central and South America—the Aztec, the Maya, the Inca. Eventually, Spanish settlers came to stay. Other explorers and colonists sailed across the Atlantic Ocean to claim the lands of the native peoples for other European nations. Ships began to travel regularly across the Atlantic Ocean. They carried not only people, but also animals and plants.

In the 1970s, a historian coined the term *Columbian Exchange* to name the exchange of living things that began when Columbus first landed on a Caribbean island. The whole world has changed in countless ways because of the Columbian Exchange.

Learn Vocabulary

Understanding vocabulary

The boxed words below are **boldfaced** in the selection. Learn the meaning of each word. Then write the word after its synonym.

colonization	
agricultural	
slaughter	
ultimately	
thrived	
cultivated	
nutritious	
staples	
plantations	

1. farmlands _____

2. finally _____

3. killing _____

4. tended _____

5. healthful _____

6. basics _____

7. prospered _____

8. settlement _____

9. farming _____

Reading Selection—Part One

Read the first part of the informational article "The Columbian Exchange."

The Columbian Exchange

ANIMALS CROSS THE ATLANTIC

Cattle. Tourism advertisements for the state of Vermont display green meadows with dairy cows contentedly grazing. No book about Texas would be complete without pictures of herds of tough longhorn cattle stirring up dust on the plains. The vast grazing lands of Kansas and Nebraska in North America, and of Argentina in South America, have made cattle-raising an essential economic activity in these regions. The beef and dairy industries are big business in the Americas. It is hard to imagine a time when cattle were not part of the landscape. Cattle, however, are not native to the Americas. The first cattle arrived in 1493, when Columbus made his second voyage to the Caribbean.

As European **colonization** expanded, some American Indians added cattle-raising to their **agricultural** activities; the Cherokees of the southeastern United States were one example. But in the western plains, a native grazing animal had long provided American Indians with meat, as well as with shelter, clothing, fuel, and more. Herds of buffalo, or American bison, were the foundation of the culture of many western tribes. After cattle ranchers came to the region, however, they were among the supporters of the **slaughter** of millions of buffalo. The great herds of buffalo were almost wiped out by the 1880s. The Plains Indians' buffalo-based culture was destroyed.

Horses. A typical image of Plains Indians is of buffalo hunters on horseback. Actually, Plains Indians were on horseback for less than 200 years. Before then, hunters pursued buffalo on foot, for there were no horses. The only beasts of burden were dogs, which carried supplies. Horses had once been native to the Americas, but they had vanished by the end of the Ice Age, thousands of years earlier. Native peoples of the Americas had never seen a horse until Spanish explorers brought the animals from Europe. Some Native Americans thought at first that a man on horseback was one beast. Others thought horses were large dogs. But ignorance quickly turned into knowledge—this animal would be useful!

Spanish officials in Mexico tried to prevent any horse trading among non-Spaniards, but native peoples were already capturing, trading, and breeding Spanish horses by the mid-1600s. Native patterns of living changed. Some people gave up farming in favor of long-distance hunting, especially of the migrating herds of buffalo. Horses came to stand for wealth and honor. Native Americans were regarded as expert riders and handlers. Some tribes, such as the Cayuse of present-day Oregon and Washington, became famous for their horse-breeding skill.

Pigs. In 1493, Columbus delivered the first European pigs to the island of Hispaniola. These sturdy animals found plenty to eat in the tropical forests and in the farmlands of the Tainos. (The Tainos were the native peoples who would be enslaved, and **ultimately** destroyed, by the Spanish conquerors.) The pigs **thrived** and reproduced rapidly. They overran the island, destroying plants and preying on native lizards and birds. When pigs were brought to the mainland, they adapted easily. Those that ran wild in the southeastern United States became known for their strength. Called razorbacks, these hogs became a food source for hunters of the region.

Other Animals. Among the other animals that Europeans introduced to the Americas were sheep, goats, and chickens. European ships also carried domestic cats, to keep the number of rats under control. When cats came ashore, many ran wild to prey on native rodents and small wildlife. Rats came ashore, too. They reproduced rapidly and adapted quickly to their new homelands.

Wild turkeys of the Americas were brought to Europe, where they were raised for food. When the first English colonists arrived in Massachusetts in 1620, they brought turkeys with them, not realizing that wild turkeys could be hunted. Another animal that travelers brought to Europe came from South America—the domestic guinea pig.

Completing an information web

Add to this information web by finding facts and details from the subsection "Cattle" in the first part of this informational article.

```
      ( first arrived in 1493,
        brought by Columbus )

( Cherokee among native
  peoples who adopted European        (            )
  practice of raising cattle )

                    ( Cattle
                      in the
                      Americas )

        (            )              (            )
```

Read the second part of the informational article "The Columbian Exchange."

PLANTS CROSS THE ATLANTIC

Potatoes. Potatoes were first **cultivated** by peoples of the Andes of South America, perhaps ten thousand years ago. Spanish explorers brought samples of the plant to Spain in the early 1500s. Eventually the plant traveled to the rest of Europe, and to Africa and Asia. Potato plants traveled to North America, too, brought by European colonists.

European rulers in Germany and Russia were the first to encourage the planting of potatoes. Potatoes could be grown fairly easily, and they were more **nutritious** than the grains that peasants were growing. Potatoes became an important food crop, not only in Germany and Russia, but also in Scandinavia, Poland, Belgium, and the Netherlands. Historians have pointed out that potatoes allowed more babies to survive to adulthood; thus, potatoes were a major cause of population growth in Europe.

Nowhere did the potato have greater impact than in Ireland. Irish farm families did not own their land. They worked for English landlords, planting grains that would be exported. To feed themselves, the Irish planted potatoes. By the 1700s, Irish peasants had become dependent on potatoes for nearly all their nutrition. Then, in 1845, disaster struck. A blight infected the potato plants. Within three years, the people had no food. More than one million Irish people died of starvation and disease. More than one million left Ireland to settle in the United States.

Today, agricultural scientists work to protect potatoes from disease. Potatoes are one of the world's four major crop **staples**.

Sugarcane. Prehistoric farmers of the Pacific island of New Guinea were the first to raise the sugarcane plant. Sugarcane is still the most important source of sucrose—the sweet substance known as sugar. In ancient times, sugarcane-farming traveled to Asia, then to the Mediterranean and North Africa.

On his second voyage to the Caribbean, Columbus brought sugarcane to Hispaniola. The islands of the Caribbean, including Cuba, Jamaica, and Puerto Rico, would soon become centers of sugarcane production. The sugarcane **plantations** required labor, and plantation owners' wish for low-cost labor led to the African slave trade. About one fourth of all the enslaved Africans who survived the Atlantic crossing were delivered to the Caribbean islands. There they were forced to perform the brutal and often deadly work of satisfying the world's desire for sweetness. Sugarcane plants arrived in the Americas, and changed history.

Other Food Plants. What would Italian cookery be without tomato sauces? Yet tomatoes were unknown in Italy before Columbus's voyages. Tomatoes were among the food crops that traveled from the Americas to Europe. Other native American crops that spread all over the globe included peanuts, cocoa, and chili peppers.

By Columbus's time, corn (also called maize) was the most important food crop in the Americas. Originally cultivated by prehistoric farmers of Mexico, corn agriculture had spread throughout the Americas. By the early 1500s, corn had crossed the Atlantic Ocean, and was being grown in West Africa. Not long after, Chinese farmers were growing corn. Today, corn is a staple crop throughout the world.

The patriotic song "America the Beautiful" begins, "Oh, beautiful, for spacious skies/for amber waves of grain." The "amber waves of grain" are wheat fields spreading as far as the eye can see. Wheat was part of the Columbian Exchange, brought to the Americas by European colonists.

Wheat, potatoes, and corn are three of the world's four staple crops. The fourth is rice. Rice was not native to the Americas, although South Carolina and other areas of the American South were to become known for rice cultivation. These rice plantations were owned by European Americans, but the methods for growing and harvesting rice were introduced by African slaves. Africans had been rice farmers for centuries by the time rice was introduced to the Americas.

Five centuries ago, plants and animals began voyaging across the Atlantic Ocean. The effects of their travels are still being felt today.

Using an information web

Fill out this information web with facts and details from the subsection "Potatoes" in the second part of the article. Then choose another subsection from either part of the informational article. On a separate piece of paper, make an information web for the subsection.

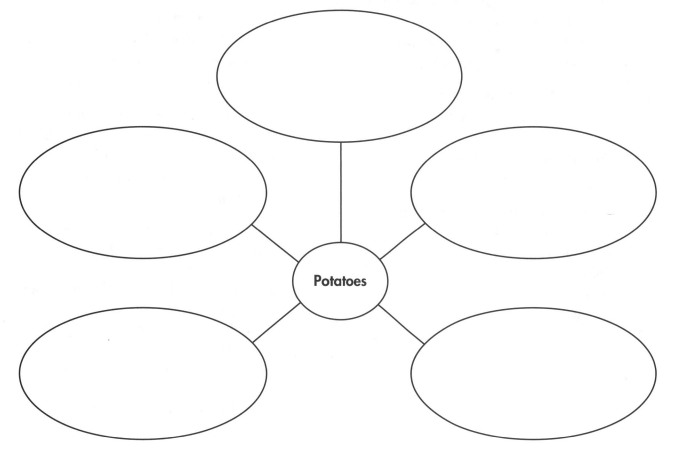

Potatoes

Check Your Understanding

Think about what you've read. Then answer these questions.

1. What herd animals supplied meat to North Americans before Columbus arrived?
   - Ⓐ pigs
   - Ⓑ horses
   - Ⓒ bison
   - Ⓓ cattle

2. When did Plains Indians probably begin to develop their horseback riding skills?
   - Ⓐ 1493 or soon afterward
   - Ⓑ about 1700
   - Ⓒ the 1880s
   - Ⓓ the early 1500s

3. According to the informational article, "European colonization expanded." What is another way of saying that?
   - Ⓐ More and more settlers from Europe arrived.
   - Ⓑ Explorers from Europe continued searching for gold and other treasures.
   - Ⓒ European rulers sponsored more voyages.
   - Ⓓ The nations of Europe grew larger.

4. What is true of an agricultural people?
   - Ⓐ They hunt on foot or horseback.
   - Ⓑ They cultivate the land.
   - Ⓒ They have a limited diet.
   - Ⓓ They follow migrating herds.

5. How many of the world's four major staple crops were native to the Americas?
   - Ⓐ all of them
   - Ⓑ one of them
   - Ⓒ three of them
   - Ⓓ half of them

6. Which of these animals was native to the Americas?
   - Ⓐ the domestic cat
   - Ⓑ dairy cows
   - Ⓒ the domestic guinea pig
   - Ⓓ razorbacks

7. Which of these statements from the article expresses an opinion?
   - Ⓐ Nowhere did the potato have greater impact than in Ireland.
   - Ⓑ Spanish explorers brought samples of the plant to Spain in the early 1500s.
   - Ⓒ European rulers in Germany and Russia were the first to encourage the planting of potatoes.
   - Ⓓ A blight infected the potato plants.

8. The development of sugarcane plantations is one reason that
   - Ⓐ people desired sweet tastes.
   - Ⓑ farmers of New Guinea cultivated the plants.
   - Ⓒ sugarcane provided sucrose.
   - Ⓓ people of African ancestry live in Jamaica.

9. Why were pigs brought to Hispaniola?
   - Ⓐ to help the conquerors overrun the island
   - Ⓑ to destroy the Tainos' crops
   - Ⓒ to prey on native lizards and birds
   - Ⓓ to feed the settlers who came with Columbus

10. Why might the author have mentioned that "amber waves of grain" is a phrase from a patriotic American song?
    - Ⓐ to point out why the Columbian Exchange is significant to patriotic people
    - Ⓑ to offer a vivid description of vast fields of wheat
    - Ⓒ to point out that Americans are singing about a foreign plant
    - Ⓓ to show respect for one's native land

11. Which of these was part of the Columbian Exchange?

Ⓐ peanuts

Ⓑ buffalo

Ⓒ dogs

Ⓓ gold

12. Why is the Columbian Exchange so important?

Ⓐ It led to population growth throughout the world.

Ⓑ It made two old and separate worlds more like one new world.

Ⓒ It led to exploration and colonization of the Americas.

Ⓓ It explains why Christopher Columbus made his voyages.

Extend Your Learning

- *Write a Paragraph of Effects*

  Write a paragraph about one of the animals that reached a new homeland as a result of the Columbian Exchange. In your paragraph, focus on the changes that the animal brought about. Tell about the effects, both immediate and long-term.

- *Research Favorite Dishes*

  Do you like pizza? What about a hamburger and a side of French fries, with plenty of ketchup? With your group, list at least five favorite dishes. Together, analyze each food to list the plants and animals that provide the ingredients. Research the origin of each ingredient. (Where was the plant or animal first domesticated?) Make a restaurant menu that includes labels showing the origin of each ingredient.

- *Find Facts and Details: Diseases*

  Plants and animals were not the only living things that were part of the Columbian Exchange. When Europeans arrived in the Americas, they brought their germs with them. Native peoples had no natural resistance to diseases such as smallpox and measles. What happened as a result? Read an informational article to find out about one or more diseases that had a terrible impact on Native Americans. Take notes about the important facts and details. Then write an informational article.

Understanding Sequence

Learn About Understanding Sequence

*Thinking about
the strategy*

Suppose someone asked you to tell what happened in last night's episode of a TV drama. You would think about the time order, or **sequence**, in which events occurred. To help your listener follow the action of the story, you would probably use sequence clue words such as *first, after that, meanwhile,* and *at the end.* Sequence clue words are useful for summing up a TV episode, recounting an experience you had, or telling a story.

To point out how events are connected in time, authors may use sequence clue words. Additional examples of sequence clue words are *next, before, during, as, afterward, then,* and *finally.* Authors may also use dates and times: *early in the morning, on July 14, late in the year 1904.* Verb tenses show sequence too: Something *is occurring, occurred, had occurred, has been occurring, will occur, would occur,* and so on.

In many texts, events are recounted out of order. An author may choose to point out something that happened earlier or may hint at what has not happened yet. As you read, look for dates, times, verb tenses, and other clues to sequence.

Studying a model

Read the passage and the notes beside it.

present

A mountain rises above the thriving, crowded city of Naples, Italy. The exceptionally fertile soil on its slopes has been farmed for many centuries. The mountain is an active volcano called Vesuvius.

Mount Vesuvius' occasional eruptions are dangers that must be accepted by Italians who choose to live in the lovely coastal region of the Bay of Naples.

past—2,000 years ago, in A.D. 79

But about 2,000 years ago—in A.D. 79—the people of the region did not even know that their mountain was a volcano. The last eruption had occurred about

even earlier past— 1200 B.C.

1200 B.C., more than one thousand years earlier. In A.D. 79, Naples (known as Neapolis) and the other cities and towns along the bay were part of the Roman Empire. The rich and powerful leaders of Rome appreciated the beauty of the bay and built grand country estates overlooking the water.

Two Roman cities of the region were Pompeii and Herculaneum. Pompeii was an active trading and business center with about 20,000 people. Smaller Herculaneum had perhaps 5,000 year-round residents, many of whom made their living by fishing. But Herculaneum was also a resort town, where wealthy Romans came to enjoy the good life in luxurious homes.

past—August 24, A.D. 79

Then, on August 24, A.D. 79, Mount Vesuvius erupted. Pompeii and Herculaneum would be buried, and eventually forgotten. Their rediscovery

more recent past—1700s

present

began in the 1700s, and excavations continue to the present day.

Learn About a Graphic Organizer

*Understanding
a timeline*

When you read any story or article that tells "what happened," keep track of the sequence of events. Note Taking with a timeline is one way to clarify or remember the sequence.

When you make a timeline, list the events in their proper time order, rather than in the order in which they are described.

The timeline below shows notes that could be taken with the passage on page 24. You can see that the first event is at the top of the line, and the last event is at the bottom. All dates mentioned in the passage are included.

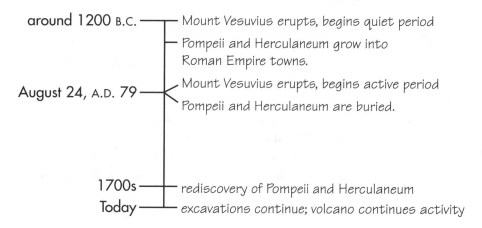

around 1200 B.C. — Mount Vesuvius erupts, begins quiet period

— Pompeii and Herculaneum grow into Roman Empire towns.

August 24, A.D. 79 — Mount Vesuvius erupts, begins active period

Pompeii and Herculaneum are buried.

1700s — rediscovery of Pompeii and Herculaneum

Today — excavations continue; volcano continues activity

The example shows events in a top-to-bottom sequence. You may prefer to show events from left to right. You may also use a different arrangement for jotting your notes on either side of the line.

A note-taking timeline does not need to be drawn to scale (with a particular length representing a number of years). But you can still use it to ask yourself questions about how much time elapsed between events. Here, for example, is a question and answer based on the example timeline:

How much time passed between the burial of Pompeii and Herculaneum and the rediscovery of the two towns?
More than 16 centuries passed between A.D. 79 and the 1700s.

As you read, ask yourself

- What clue words, dates, and times are given?
- Is the time shifting between past and present?
- Are there hints about events to come?

Learn About a Form of Writing

Any story that tells what happened is called a narrative, and has a beginning, a middle, and an end. The author narrates the events, taking readers step by step through the action. The author may skip around in time—to add interest, to build suspense, or to explain earlier events.

A narrative may be fictional—made up by the author. In a **nonfiction narrative**, the events really happened. A nonfiction narrative is also called a true story. Some nonfiction narratives take readers to an unfamiliar setting. If an author is narrating a story about something that happened long ago, for example, background information may be worked into the story so that readers can follow the action with understanding.

The author of a nonfiction narrative is giving factual information and telling a story at the same time. As you read, form pictures in your mind. Try to imagine yourself in that place and time. Think about how you would feel and what you might do. Get involved in the action.

*Organizing ideas
in a timeline*

In a nonfiction narrative, sequence matters. Pay attention to sequence clue words, dates and times, verb tenses, and any shifts in time. Use a timeline to list the events in the order in which they occurred, rather than in the order in which they are narrated. That way, you can identify the key events and follow the action.

First	Then	After that	Next	Finally
Event is listed here.	Event is listed here.	Event is listed here.	Event is listed here.	Event is listed here.

Prepare for the Reading Selection

Gaining knowledge

The pages that follow contain a nonfiction narrative titled "Lost for Centuries." It tells about a disastrous event in A.D. 79. Two cities of ancient Rome—Pompeii and Herculaneum— were suddenly buried by material that erupted from the volcano Mount Vesuvius.

This map shows places that are discussed in the narrative.

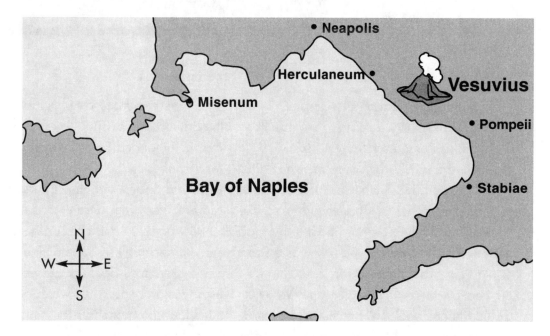

As you find these place names and directions in the selection, refer to the map.

The passage on page 24 serves as an introduction, which you may want to reread first for background information.

Learn Vocabulary

Understanding vocabulary

The boxed words below are **boldfaced** in the selection. Learn the meaning of each word. Then write the word beside its clue.

scholar

bombarded

pumice

debris

tremors

molten

excavation

systematic

reconstructed

1. This is an archaeologist's "dig." _____

2. Hailstones or cannon balls did this. _____

3. A volcano produces this. _____

4. This word describes liquid rock. _____

5. This was done to an object that was destroyed. _____

6. This person likes to learn. _____

7. This can describe a workable plan. _____

8. Feel these underfoot during an earthquake. _____

9. An explosion leaves this behind. _____

Read the first part of the nonfiction narrative "Lost for Centuries."

Lost for Centuries

Early in the afternoon of August 24, A.D. 79, a 17-year-old boy and his mother watched a large white and black cloud rising to the east across the Bay of Naples. The boy was the nephew of Pliny (PLIN ee), a Roman **scholar** and scientist. Pliny also commanded Rome's naval fleet. The boy and his mother were visiting at Misenum, where Pliny was stationed.

When the boy's mother pointed out the strange cloud, it aroused Pliny's curiosity. He climbed to a high spot to see better. The cloud looked like a gigantic tree, with a trunk that split off into branches. Pliny immediately ordered a boat to be readied—he wanted to get a closer look. He invited his nephew to join him, but the boy was a serious student and preferred to continue reading and writing.

As Pliny was preparing to leave, he received an urgent message. People were gathering along the coast to the southeast of Mount Vesuvius, which was erupting. They were trying to escape by sea. Could the navy help? Pliny immediately ordered the launching of ships for a rescue mission. He boarded one of the ships, and they headed into danger.

As the ships drew near the coast, they were **bombarded** with **pumice** stones falling from a black sky. Hot cinders blew down. The sea churned, and coastal waters became suddenly shallow. There could be no landing place on the shores, which were already buried under **debris** from the volcano. Pliny directed the ships to land farther south, at Stabiae. There, Pliny went to the house of a friend, and tried to reassure the frightened family that all would be well. It was early evening, the usual bedtime for Romans, so Pliny lay down to sleep.

The other people in the house were too terrified to sleep. The earth trembled. Lightning flashed. Fires burned. The level of ashes grew higher and higher in the courtyard. By early morning, the buildings had begun to shake and sway. The sun had risen, but the town lay under smoky darkness. Stones dropped continuously from the sky. The family awakened Pliny. Would it be safer indoors or out? They decided to go outside, but first they put pillows on their heads for protection. Pliny reached the shore, but the waves were so wild, no boat could be launched. Fire was approaching, and the air was thick with poisonous fumes. Pliny's throat felt parched, and he breathed with difficulty. He lay down to rest briefly, stood up, then collapsed. He was dead.

About 18 hours earlier, around noon of August 24, the people of Pompeii were going about their usual routines, though not in an entirely carefree way. Things felt wrong. Early that morning, a dusting of light ash had come from the direction of Vesuvius. The night before, the earth had shaken again. For weeks there had been **tremors**. Wells had dried abruptly. Dogs barked at nothing. On August 20, the earth had shaken with particular violence. At that time, some people left the city. They remembered the great deadly earthquake that had occurred 17 years earlier. It had been so destructive that the rebuilding was still going on. Perhaps another earthquake was coming.

Shortly after noon, the top of Vesuvius blew right off. An enormous explosion shook Pompeii. **Molten** rock shot high into the sky. It spread out as it fell earthward, forming a giant cloud that looked like a kind of tree trunk with branches to observers at Misenum, nearly 20 miles across the bay.

High in the atmosphere, the winds blew southeast, sending the mighty cloud toward Pompeii. The sky turned dark. Choking ash and lightweight pumice stones fell like snow and hail on the streets. Red-hot stones heavy enough to kill also hurtled from the sky. Within a few hours, the streets were buried under ash and stone. Walls and structures were tumbling. Most of the people had fled to neighboring towns. About 2,000 people did not make it out of Pompeii. By the time Pliny's ships passed by the coast, unable to attempt a rescue, the people were either dead, or dying imprisoned in the buried rooms where they had sought shelter.

Completing a timeline   Review the events in the first part of the nonfiction narrative. Then add entries to this timeline.

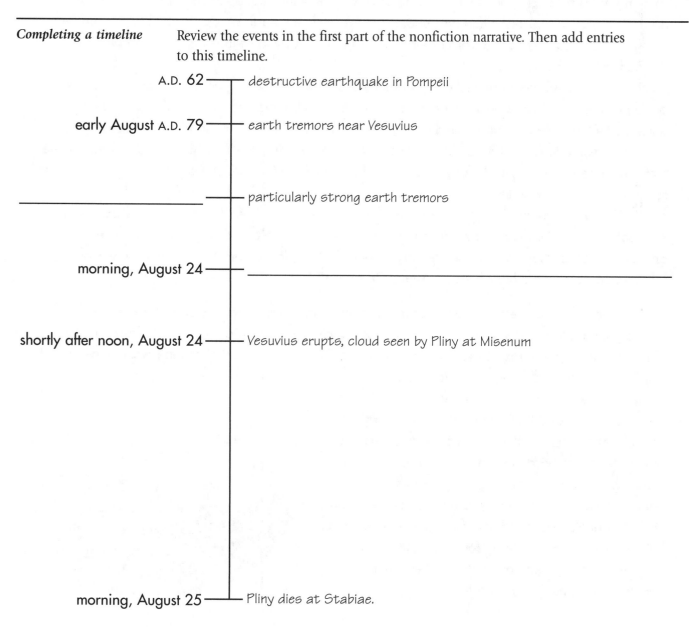

A.D. 62 ——┬— destructive earthquake in Pompeii

early August A.D. 79 ——┼— earth tremors near Vesuvius

————————————— ——┼— particularly strong earth tremors

morning, August 24 ——┼— ————————————————————

shortly after noon, August 24 ——┼— Vesuvius erupts, cloud seen by Pliny at Misenum

morning, August 25 ——┴— Pliny dies at Stabiae.

Read the second part of the nonfiction narrative "Lost for Centuries."

While Pompeii was being buried under ash and pumice, the people of Herculaneum had time to escape. Many did escape. But others stayed where they were, watching the vast cloud from the volcano, and hoping that the winds would continue to keep it away from their town.

Just after midnight on the morning of August 25, Vesuvius let loose its deadliest surprise. A pyroclastic flow—a high-speed, low-lying cloud of steam, ash, and rock fragments—raced down the slopes of the volcano and headed straight for Herculaneum. Within minutes, the town was buried. Every person and animal in it was instantly killed. The heat was so intense that only their scorched bones remained. Modern researchers estimate that the temperature of the pyroclastic flow was about 900 degrees Fahrenheit (500°C).

What of Pliny's sister and her son, who had stayed behind in Misenum? The nephew, who had the same name as his uncle and would become known as Pliny the Younger, had continued to study after his uncle's departure. He still had his head in a book while the earth shook and buildings shuddered. As August 25 began, and the walls around them seemed ready to collapse, the boy and his mother decided to try to escape.

They saw the sea being sucked away from the shore by the quaking earth. A monstrous black cloud bursting with flames hugged the land and seemed to be heading right for them. Shrieks and wails from a terror-stricken mob filled the darkness. The mother told her son to save himself and to leave her behind to die—she was old and could not run. But Pliny the Younger stayed with his mother through the terrifying night. When dawn broke, they could see the sun. The dangerous cloud had not reached them, and Misenum would survive.

Years later, a Roman historian asked Pliny the Younger to tell about the eruption of Vesuvius and the death of Pliny the Elder. Pliny the Younger, a well-known scholar by that time, wrote letters based on his own recollections and reports he had gathered. Those letters remain priceless sources of information about what happened on August 24 and 25 in A.D. 79.

As the centuries passed, the buried cities of Pompeii and Herculaneum were forgotten. Another village grew on top of Herculaneum, and in 1709, a villager digging a deep well discovered stones of the ancient city. The report reached the ruling Austrian prince, who directed the first **excavation**, with the purpose of digging up ancient treasures.

In the nineteenth century, archaeologists (rather than treasure hunters and looters) began the **systematic** and scientific excavation of Pompeii and Herculaneum. The volcanic ash had hardened and acted as a preserving material. Everything was exactly as it had been. Ancient Roman towns were revealed in a unique and fascinating way. Archaeologists found not just streets and buildings, but loaves of bread, plates of food, gardening tools, jewelry, sculptures, wall paintings, and everything the people had left behind as they fled.

In Pompeii, archaeologists discovered that powdery volcanic ash hardening around a body preserved the shape and the surface details long after the body itself had decayed. The ash created a kind of mold. By pouring plaster into the mold, and then chipping away at the outer covering, archaeologists could make the bodies of Vesuvius' victims "reappear." Thus, the final moments of Pompeii's people and animals were **reconstructed**.

Because excavations at Herculaneum produced few human remains, archaeologists long believed that the town had been abandoned at the time of the eruption. But in the 1980s, large numbers of skeletons were found. They showed groups of people who had sought safety by the shore but had been killed instantly by the pyroclastic flow.

At the start of the twenty-first century, archaeologists continue to dig and learn. More of Pompeii has been uncovered than of Herculaneum, which lies more deeply buried. These two ancient cities are no longer lost, but there is still much to find.

Using a timeline

Use the space below to draw a timeline with events from the second part of the nonfiction narrative. Tell what happened at Herculaneum and at Misenum. End the timeline with events from the present.

Check Your Understanding

Think about what you've read. Then answer these questions.

1. Which of these events happened first?
   - Ⓐ the death of Pliny
   - Ⓑ the destruction of Herculaneum
   - Ⓒ the destruction of Pompeii
   - Ⓓ the pyroclastic flow from Vesuvius

2. Why had some people already left Pompeii by the time Vesuvius erupted?
   - Ⓐ Events earlier in August had made them fear that a great earthquake was coming.
   - Ⓑ They knew from the experience 17 years before that the volcano was about to erupt.
   - Ⓒ They had sought safety in Herculaneum.
   - Ⓓ They had been rescued by ships of the Roman navy.

3. What is an example of debris from Vesuvius?
   - Ⓐ tremors
   - Ⓑ death
   - Ⓒ pumice
   - Ⓓ lightning

4. Because Pliny the Elder was a scholar, the sight of the strange cloud made him
   - Ⓐ want to find out more about it.
   - Ⓑ feel confused and troubled.
   - Ⓒ act with great courage.
   - Ⓓ behave foolishly.

5. When Pliny the Younger and his mother were trying to survive a terrifying night, what was Pliny the Elder doing?
   - Ⓐ dying
   - Ⓑ landing at Stabiae
   - Ⓒ sleeping
   - Ⓓ sailing past the destruction at Pompeii

6. What was the probable cause of Pliny the Elder's death?
   - Ⓐ the intense heat
   - Ⓑ the poisonous gases
   - Ⓒ the pyroclastic flow
   - Ⓓ the ash cloud

7. On August 24, what was true in Herculaneum?
   - Ⓐ The town was buried under powdery volcanic ash.
   - Ⓑ Everyone was killed instantly.
   - Ⓒ Frightened people gathered to escape by sea.
   - Ⓓ Most people had left the town.

8. In the early hours of August 25, how did Pliny the Younger probably feel?
   - Ⓐ greatly relieved that he and his mother had survived
   - Ⓑ grief-stricken by his uncle's death
   - Ⓒ terrified by the black cloud bursting with flames
   - Ⓓ eager to return to his studies

9. Why does the author use the word *priceless* to describe Pliny the Younger's letters?
   - Ⓐ The letters are extremely valuable sources of information.
   - Ⓑ The letters give a scholar's explanation of why Vesuvius erupted.
   - Ⓒ The letters give the account of someone who was in Pompeii and lived to tell about it.
   - Ⓓ The letters are in a historical collection and will never be sold.

10. Less of Herculaneum has been excavated than of Pompeii. One likely reason is that
    - Ⓐ there are fewer treasures in Herculaneum.
    - Ⓑ Vesuvius still poses a threat.
    - Ⓒ Pompeii is the more famous of the two sites.
    - Ⓓ it is easier to dig in Pompeii.

11. How are the excavations by archaeologists more systematic than those of treasure hunters?

Ⓐ Treasure hunters are actually stealing.

Ⓑ Archaeologists are more educated than treasure hunters.

Ⓒ Archaeologists dig carefully and keep records.

Ⓓ Treasure hunters take only valuable items.

12. What can people today learn from Pompeii and Herculaneum?

Ⓐ how to stay safe from volcanic eruptions

Ⓑ how far the Roman Empire spread

Ⓒ why natural disasters bring changes

Ⓓ what typical ancient Roman towns were like

Extend Your Learning

- *Write a News Bulletin*

  "We interrupt this program to bring you an important news bulletin." What if news bulletins existed in A.D. 79? Write the imaginary news bulletin that tells listeners or viewers about the horrifying event that is happening in the Bay of Naples. Make sure to include the date and time.

- *Plan an Interview with Pliny the Younger*

  With your group, find sources that include the letters Pliny the Younger wrote about the eruption of Vesuvius. Write questions about the events, and use excerpts from the letters as answers. You may turn the "interview" into a performance by having group members take turns playing the parts of the interviewer and Pliny the Younger.

- *Research Pompeii and Herculaneum Today*

  The author of "Lost for Centuries" says that discoveries are still being made at Pompeii and Herculaneum. Use library databases to find a recently published book or magazine article, or a current news article about Pompeii, Herculaneum, or both. Read about recent discoveries. Make a timeline to show the sequence of events.

Recognizing Cause and Effect

Learn About Recognizing Cause and Effect

Thinking about the strategy

Whenever you ask or answer a question beginning with *why*, you are thinking about causes and effects. A **cause** is why something happens. An **effect** is what happens. Authors writing about historical events and science concepts frequently highlight causes and effects. Cause-effect relationships are part of just about any informational topic in which there are connections among events.

In the following sentences, the causes are underlined once and the effects are underlined twice. Notice that although a cause leads to an effect, the cause is not always in the first position.

- Ice crystals building up in the crack of a rock can cause the rock to break apart.
- Rocks also break apart because of changes between hot and cold temperatures.
- Plant roots dig into small cracks in rocks, and the rocks break as a result.
- Rocks also break as a consequence of human activities such as blasting.
- Rocks become smaller and smaller over time and eventually combine with organic material to form soil.

You can see cause-effect clue words in the sentences above. Words such as *cause*, *because*, and *reason* point to causes. Words such as *result*, *so*, and *consequence* point to effects. Clue words are not always given, however, as shown in the last sentence above.

Studying a model

Read the paragraph and the notes beside it.

Cause-effect clue words:
reason
so
Because
result

Main cause-effect connection:
The tilt of the northern hemisphere toward the sun causes summer in that hemisphere.

In the northern hemisphere, the season of summer brings long days and hot temperatures. The reason is not, as many people believe, that Earth is closest to the sun during summer. The reason is the tilt of the spinning Earth as it orbits the sun. During part of its year-long journey around the sun, Earth's northern hemisphere is tilted toward the sun. The sun's energy strikes that hemisphere at a high angle. Any light source that shines directly above a surface provides more concentrated energy, so the high angle of the sun means greater energy on that section of Earth's surface. Because the energy also has less atmosphere to travel through, more of it is able to reach the surface instead of being absorbed or bounced back into space. As a result, the northern hemisphere has the season called summer.

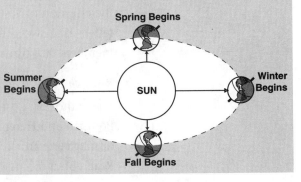

34

Learn About a Graphic Organizer

*Understanding
a cause-effect
diagram*

As you read about why things happen, think about how causes lead to effects. You can see the connections directly if you make a special drawing, or diagram, in which arrows point from causes to effects. You can also see how an effect can turn into the cause for another effect.

This **cause-effect diagram** shows cause-effect connections from the paragraph on page 34.

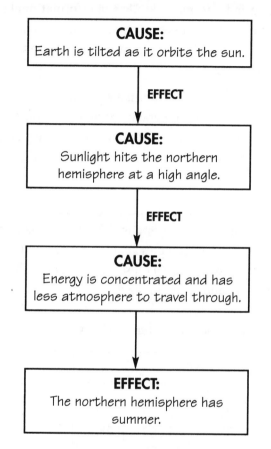

The information in a cause-effect diagram can be used in a summary statement. Notice how a cause-effect clue word appears in the statement:

The northern hemisphere has summer at the time of year that it is tilted toward the sun.

As you read, ask yourself

- What happens?
- Why does it happen?
- What happens as a result?

Learn About a Form of Writing

Focusing on an informational article: science

Science topics cover life forms, physical matter and events, technology—just about everything in the universe, including the universe itself. You can find articles on science topics in print and on-line. They appear in magazines and newspapers, in nonfiction books, and in encyclopedias.

Although science topics have an enormous range, science authors share the general purpose of explaining and informing. Readers of **informational science articles** learn about processes, such as the water cycle or photosynthesis; and about systems, such as an ocean food web or the workings of a computer. Science articles explain the answers to all sorts of *why* questions.

Science articles often have graphical information as well as text. Numerical data and patterns may be shown in charts and graphs. Systems and processes may be explained with special drawings called diagrams. To understand these graphic aids, start by reading the title and captions. Ask yourself what the aid is illustrating, and try to summarize the information in it.

Organizing ideas in a cause-effect diagram

Because science articles often answer *why* questions, they explain cause-effect connections. Draw a cause-effect diagram to take notes about those connections. Keep in mind that there is no single correct way to make a cause-effect diagram. The diagram should match the organization of causes and effects in the text. Here are just three possible arrangements.

One cause may lead to several effects.

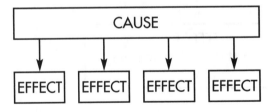

Several causes may lead to just one effect.

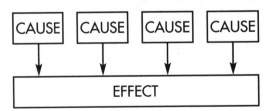

In a cause-effect chain, each effect turns into a cause.

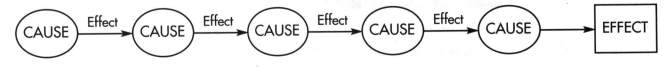

Prepare for the Reading Selection

Gaining knowledge

The scientific study of weather is called meteorology. Meteorologists gather and interpret data about the atmosphere—the layers of air that surround planet Earth. Weather depends largely on events that occur in the densest layer of the atmosphere, the layer that is closest to the surface of Earth—the troposphere.

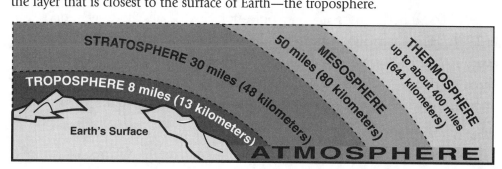

Modern meteorologists use a variety of methods to gather data: satellites that orbit Earth, balloons with measuring devices, weather stations in every part of the world, specially equipped planes that fly into storms, and more. The atmosphere is an extremely complicated setting. Heat from the sun, moisture from the oceans, the rotation of Earth, currents in water and air, and many other factors influence weather. Although meteorologists have a great deal of knowledge about how these factors influence one another, predicting the changes that will occur in the atmosphere is never a simple task.

The pages that follow contain an article about hurricanes, the most powerful storms on the earth. Meteorologists can tell when and where a hurricane is forming, but predicting the path and power of a hurricane is a major challenge.

Learn Vocabulary

Understanding vocabulary

The boxed words below are **boldfaced** in the selection. Learn the meaning of each word. Then complete the sentence with the word that fits in the blank.

immeasurable
tropical
dense
counterclockwise
spiral
torrential
mudslides
catastrophic
evacuation
erosion

1. The regions on either side of the equator are the _____ zones.

2. To take people away from danger, communities have plans for

   _____ .

3. A winding staircase is in the shape of a _____ .

4. A _____ event causes terrible destruction.

5. The sandy beach vanished as a result of _____ .

6. Houses on the hillside were buried under _____ .

7. It is not possible to count something that is _____ .

8. The dancer turned her face to the left and twirled _____ .

9. Warm air is light in weight, but cold air is heavy and _____ .

10. A waterfall and a downpour are both _____ .

37

Reading Selection—Part One

Read the first part of the informational article "Hurricane!"

Hurricane!

In 1900, a hurricane slams into Galveston, Texas, kills thousands, and destroys much of the city. In 1988, Hurricane Gilbert strikes the West Indies and Mexico and is declared the most intense storm ever recorded in the Western Hemisphere. In 1998, Central America falls victim to Hurricane Mitch. These hurricanes are just a few that have brought death and terror to millions of people, and **immeasurable** destruction to property. Hurricanes are among the worst natural disasters in the world.

What is a hurricane?

The term *hurricane* applies to storms that form over the Atlantic Ocean or the Northeast Pacific Ocean. (In other ocean regions, the same kinds of storms are called typhoons or tropical cyclones.) Hurricanes have powerful, swirling winds. These storms get their strength from the sea. They travel, can stretch hundreds of miles across, and may last many days.

How does a hurricane form?

When **tropical** ocean waters are at their warmest, hurricane season occurs. For North Americans, hurricanes are most likely during the summer and early fall. A hurricane can form when the tropical ocean has a surface temperature greater than 80 degrees Fahrenheit (26.5°C). That top layer of warm water evaporates (changes to the gas called water vapor) and makes the air moist.

Warm air is less **dense** than cooler air, so the moist, heated air rises. It reaches the cooler air higher in the atmosphere. Whenever warm air and cool air meet, the result is condensation—the opposite of evaporation. Water vapor condenses into water droplets. Rain clouds form. The process of condensation releases heat energy. The newly heated air rises still farther.

Rising air creates an area of low pressure. Air masses move out of high-pressure areas and into low-pressure areas. The movement is a familiar one—it is called wind. Above the warm ocean, wind sweeps in a circular motion into the column of air. The circular motion is one result of Earth's constant spinning, which forces wind into curved paths. In the northern hemisphere, wind swirls around a low-pressure area in a **counterclockwise** direction. This swirling wind brings yet more moisture from the ocean to the growing thunderstorms above.

The clouds form a **spiral** shape around a central hole. When meteorologists determine that the winds are spinning faster than 38 miles (61 kilometers) per hour, they call the formation a tropical storm. If the winds swirl ever faster, reaching speeds greater than 74 miles (119 kilometers) per hour, the storm is upgraded to a hurricane.

In order for the hurricane to avoid fading, it must continue to get energy from the condensation of water vapor. The central area of low pressure must continue to pull in the surrounding high-pressure air. Winds usually blow at different speeds at different levels in the atmosphere. But in a hurricane, the winds continue to swirl at similar speeds at all levels. A hurricane is an unusual storm system.

Parts of a Hurricane

The calm center is called the eye.
It is the area of lowest pressure.

The fastest, most powerful winds surround
the eye. They form the eye wall.

Thunderstorms form rain bands that
extend outward from the center.

Warm, moist air spirals upward.
Cool air drops through the eye.
The entire storm system spins.
Average hurricanes are 300 miles wide.

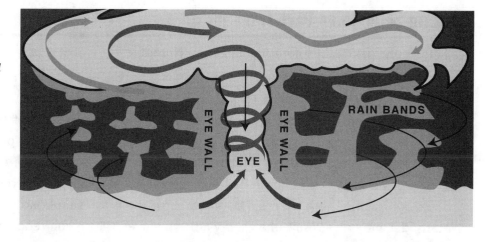

Completing a
cause-effect diagram

Fill out this diagram with causes and effects from the section "How does a hurricane form?" Use the causes and effects listed below, after putting them in the correct order.

- Wind sweeps into the low-pressure area left behind.
- Moist, heated air rises.
- Warm tropical waters evaporate.
- Wind speeds increase to 75 miles per hour—hurricane.
- Clouds spiral around a central hole.
- Rain clouds and thunderstorms form.
- Condensation occurs at higher, cooler layers of the atmosphere.
- Tropical storm forms.

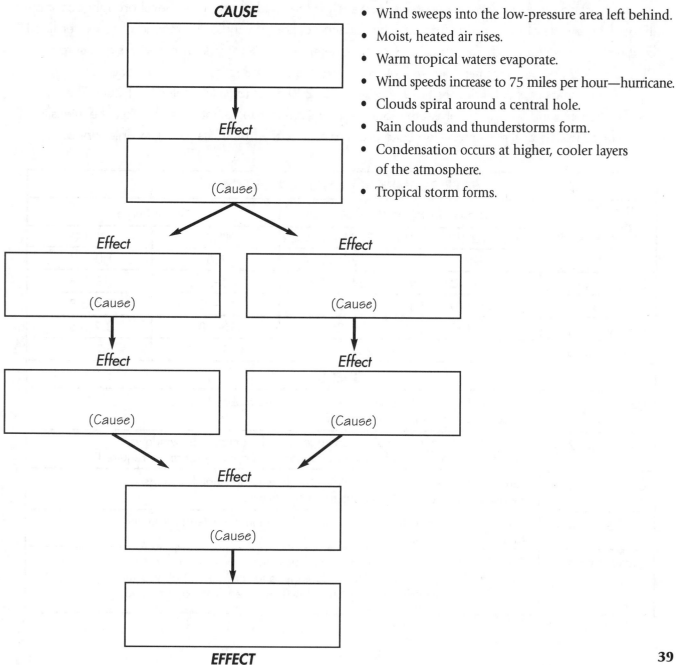

Reading Selection—Part Two

Read the second part of the informational article "Hurricane!"

What are some effects of hurricanes?

Hurricanes are dangerous to ships at sea, but modern forecasting methods enable most ships to get out of the way. (A hurricane has high-speed winds, but it does not generally travel at high speeds.) Hurricanes are most destructive when they strike land because that is where people and property are.

The powerful winds of hurricanes rip roofs off houses, topple trees and lampposts, and smash boats against the shore. The rain during a hurricane is **torrential** and often causes flooding. **Mudslides** may also result. The wind whips up waves, which can reach great heights as they crash into the shore. Tornadoes may also form. Tornadoes, like hurricanes, are made of high-speed spinning winds. Tornado winds are even faster than those of hurricanes. Unlike hurricanes, tornadoes are small and last only a short time.

The most damaging part of a hurricane, however, is the sudden rise in sea level brought about by the sucking effects of low air pressure and the carrying action of winds. The mound of seawater lifted by the hurricane can reach heights of 20 feet (6 meters) or more. This rise is called a storm surge. During a storm surge, a tremendous wall of water crashes over beaches, dwellings, and streets.

The most **catastrophic** hurricanes have winds of over 200 miles (320 kilometers) per hour. The combination of wind speed, low pressure readings, and storm-surge height is used to rate the intensity of a hurricane. The Saffir-Simpson Hurricane Scale rates intensity from Category 1 to Category 5.

SAFFIR-SIMPSON HURRICANE SCALE				
Category (level)	**Maximum Sustained Wind Speed**		**Storm Surge**	
	MILES PER HOUR	KILOMETERS PER HOUR	FEET	METERS
1 (weak)	74–95	119–153	3–5	1.0–1.7
2 (moderate)	96–110	154–177	6–8	1.8–2.6
3 (strong)	111–130	178–209	9–12	2.7–3.8
4 (very strong)	131–155	210–250	13–18	3.9–5.6
5 (devastating)	156+	251+	19+	5.7+

EFFECTS	
CATEGORY 1	Damage mainly to shrubbery, trees, leaves, and mobile homes. Flooding of low-lying coastal areas.
CATEGORY 2	Some trees blown down. Some damage to roofing materials, windows, and doors. **Evacuation** of some coastal homes and low-lying areas required.
CATEGORY 3	Large trees blown down. Some structural damage to small buildings. Mobile homes destroyed. Serious flooding at coast.
CATEGORY 4	Roofs on many small houses destroyed. Flooding may extend far inland. Major beach **erosion**.
CATEGORY 5	Roofs blown off. Extensive shattering of glass in windows and doors. Small buildings overturned. Major damage to lower floors of all structures near shoreline. Massive evacuation of low-lying areas may be required.

What can people do to protect themselves from hurricanes?

In the United States, meteorologists of the National Weather Service monitor storm systems closely. They issue a *hurricane watch* for locations that may be affected by a hurricane within 36 hours. People in those locations can log on to weather Web sites, watch television, and listen to the radio for updates. If the storm is likely to strike land within 24 hours, a *hurricane warning* is issued.

People should follow hurricane safety procedures to protect themselves and their property. Every home should be equipped with plywood and masking tape for securing windows so that glass does not shatter. Every resident should know how to shut off the water, gas, and electricity—and should know never to touch the electric power switch while standing in water!

In addition, homes should have flashlights and battery-powered radios, and plenty of batteries to keep them running. Candles and matches are also important. Several days' supply of canned foods and foods that don't need refrigeration are also needed, as are clean, airtight containers to store drinking water. A first-aid kit should be well-stocked and easily reached.

Houses and other structures in U.S. coastal areas must be built according to codes that increase their likelihood of withstanding hurricanes. There are no guarantees, however. If the hurricane is particularly intense, roofs may blow off, walls may collapse, and a storm surge may flood whole neighborhoods. If such destruction seems likely, residents will be asked to evacuate their homes and move to designated shelters before the storm hits. Evacuation routes have been set up in all states that may be reached by hurricanes.

Because a hurricane is fueled by water vapor from the sea, it runs out of energy if it stays inland. But before it dies, it can turn towns into wastelands and leave lasting memories of terror.

Using a cause-effect diagram

Use the information in the second part of the article to draw a cause-effect diagram of your own design or use the one your teacher gives you. Choose one of these questions to answer in your diagram:

- What parts of a hurricane cause damage, and what damage is caused?
- What are hurricane-safety precautions and the reason for each one?

Check Your Understanding

Think about what you've read. Then answer these questions.

1. Why can ships at sea usually avoid getting caught in a hurricane?
   Ⓐ Hurricanes form over land, not water.
   Ⓑ Hurricane winds are slower over the sea.
   Ⓒ Marine weather forecasts are more accurate than land forecasts.
   Ⓓ Ships have time to get out of the hurricane's path.

2. What is a main reason for the buildup in energy that powers a hurricane?
   Ⓐ Clouds stretch hundreds of miles across.
   Ⓑ Earth is constantly spinning.
   Ⓒ The central area of a hurricane has the lowest air pressure.
   Ⓓ Water changes to vapor and then changes back to water.

3. Why is a Category 5 hurricane likely to be catastrophic?
   Ⓐ The storm can overturn buildings.
   Ⓑ There may be flooding of low-lying coastal areas.
   Ⓒ People should leave the area.
   Ⓓ Meteorologists cannot predict the exact path of the hurricane.

4. The diagram on page 39 shows cool air falling through the eye of the hurricane. Why does it fall?
   Ⓐ It is carrying water vapor.
   Ⓑ It is denser than the warm air.
   Ⓒ It has lower pressure than the eye.
   Ⓓ Strong winds in the eye are blowing the cold air downward.

5. What is always true of torrential rains?
   Ⓐ They are accompanied by strong winds.
   Ⓑ They drop great quantities of water in a short period of time.
   Ⓒ They cause mudslides.
   Ⓓ They are caused by hurricanes.

6. What is a main difference between a hurricane and a tornado?
   Ⓐ A hurricane is much bigger than a tornado.
   Ⓑ Hurricane winds are much faster than tornado winds.
   Ⓒ Only a tornado has high-speed whirling winds.
   Ⓓ Tornadoes do not have enough energy to knock down buildings.

7. The hurricane in 1900 killed thousands of people in the island city of Galveston, Texas. What was the likeliest cause of death?
   Ⓐ flying debris
   Ⓑ erosion
   Ⓒ drowning
   Ⓓ lightning from thunderstorms

8. When is a hurricane most likely to occur in the northern hemisphere?
   Ⓐ December
   Ⓑ March
   Ⓒ May
   Ⓓ September

9. What is a likely effect of a hurricane?
   Ⓐ drops in ocean surface temperatures under the storm
   Ⓑ expansion of the atmosphere
   Ⓒ a tropical storm
   Ⓓ movement of air masses from high pressure to low pressure

10. Suppose that in the midst of a fierce hurricane, the wind suddenly changes to a gentle breeze and the sky turns clear. What is the likeliest explanation?
    Ⓐ The hurricane has traveled too far inland and is fading.
    Ⓑ The eye of the hurricane is traveling over the area.
    Ⓒ The storm surge is occurring.
    Ⓓ The winds are shifting to turn counterclockwise.

11. Which of these statements expresses a main idea of the informational article?

Ⓐ The Saffir-Simpson Hurricane Scale is used to rate hurricane intensity.

Ⓑ Hurricanes can topple trees and lampposts.

Ⓒ Hurricanes form only over oceans.

Ⓓ Thunderstorms are a feature of hurricanes.

12. If a hurricane watch is issued by the National Weather Service for your area, what should you do?

Ⓐ Make sure you have batteries, canned food, and other needed supplies.

Ⓑ Follow the evacuation route to a shelter.

Ⓒ Make sure your house is built to up-to-date codes.

Ⓓ Turn off your electricity, gas, and water.

Extend Your Learning

- *Write a Hurricane Description*

  Use print and on-line sources to find images of hurricanes and their effects. (The National Oceanic and Atmospheric Administration's Web site is one source: www.noaa.gov.) Choose one picture. Write at least one paragraph to describe it. Use exact and vivid words.

- *Research Record-breaking Hurricanes*

  What are the most significant hurricanes in history? Why is each so noteworthy? With other group members, research hurricane history. Make an illustrated chart in which you give the facts and details.

- *Learn About the Whys of Weather*

  Choose a weather phenomenon: a thunderstorm, a hailstorm, sweltering heat, or something else that interests you. Read a book or an article about the topic. Make a cause-effect diagram to show the reasons for that kind of weather.

Comparing and Contrasting

Learn About Comparing and Contrasting

Thinking about the strategy

Telling how things are alike is called **comparing**. Words such as *both, like, all, similar,* and *in common* are clues to comparisons. Pointing out differences is called **contrasting**. Words such as *different, however, but, unlike,* and *on the other hand* are often clues to contrasts. Words such as *more* and *less,* and the endings *-er* and *-est* also signal comparisons and contrasts.

Authors point out comparisons and contrasts so that the reader can understand how people, places, things, and ideas are alike and different.

Thoughtful readers make their own comparisons and contrasts, too—thinking about how two works by the same author are alike and different, for example, or about how different authors treat the same topic.

Studying a model

Read the passage and the notes beside it.

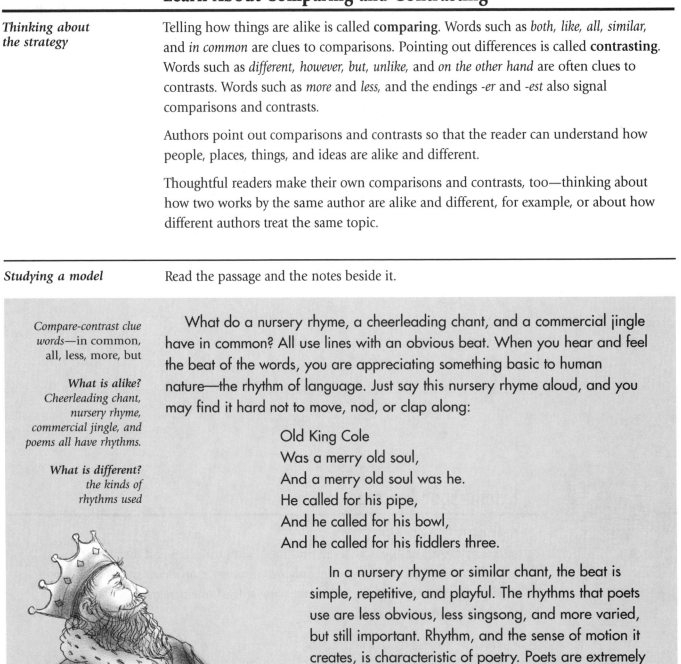

Compare-contrast clue words—in common, all, less, more, but

What is alike? Cheerleading chant, nursery rhyme, commercial jingle, and poems all have rhythms.

What is different? the kinds of rhythms used

What do a nursery rhyme, a cheerleading chant, and a commercial jingle have in common? All use lines with an obvious beat. When you hear and feel the beat of the words, you are appreciating something basic to human nature—the rhythm of language. Just say this nursery rhyme aloud, and you may find it hard not to move, nod, or clap along:

Old King Cole
Was a merry old soul,
And a merry old soul was he.
He called for his pipe,
And he called for his bowl,
And he called for his fiddlers three.

In a nursery rhyme or similar chant, the beat is simple, repetitive, and playful. The rhythms that poets use are less obvious, less singsong, and more varied, but still important. Rhythm, and the sense of motion it creates, is characteristic of poetry. Poets are extremely sensitive to the rhythms of their lines. The rhythm—which is connected to the pattern of stressed and unstressed syllables and line length—helps to convey the mood and meaning of the whole poem.

Learn About a Graphic Organizer

In some nonfiction writings, similarities and differences are important ideas. For example, you may be reading to learn how the views of two political candidates differ, or how a consumer report rates different products. An informational article may compare and contrast a hurricane and a tornado, or life before and after the invention of cars, or two geographic regions of a country, or just about any other topic. Whenever you read texts in which similarities and differences are important, you can take notes in a way that points out those ideas.

This **compare-contrast diagram** shows notes about the passage on page 44.

Differences	Similarities	Differences
Rhythms of nursery rhymes, chants, jingles		**Rhythms of poetry**
lines have obvious beat	are basic to human nature	are less obvious and singsong
clap or nod along to it	are important to meaning	are more varied
simple, repetitive, playful	are heard and felt	are connected to pattern of stressed and unstressed syllables and line length
	create a sense of motion	help to convey mood and meaning of the poem

In school assignments and tests, you will be asked to write compare-contrast paragraphs or essays. A compare-contrast diagram can help you organize your ideas for writing.

As you read, ask yourself

- Which clue words signal how things are alike?
- Which clue words signal how things are different?
- Is the topic a category of some kind? Is the author pointing out any differences within the category?

Learn About a Form of Writing

Focusing on a poem

What makes a **poem** different from other forms of writing? For one thing, it looks different on a page. A poem is set off in lines, usually of varying length. More important, however, is that a poem should be read differently from other forms of writing.

The meaning and the mood of a poem are linked to sound. That is why it is helpful to read a poem aloud. Listen for the rhythm of the lines and the sounds in the words. You may hear repeated sounds or repeated words. You may hear end rhymes (through/new, hairy/scary), especially in traditional kinds of poems.

Remember that the poet spent time choosing exactly the right words to put down in a particular way. To appreciate the poem, you need to read it more than once. Each time, try to form pictures in your mind. Listen for new things. Make "I wonder why" statements about the poem; for example: "I wonder why the poem has such short lines." "I wonder why the poet makes that comparison." With practice, you can come up with likely reasons and answers.

Poets often see things in terms of other things. A flowing brook may "chatter" like a person, for example. A happy feeling may be compared to the soaring of a bird. Notice such figurative comparisons as you read, and you will strengthen your sense of the poem's meaning.

Organizing ideas in a compare-contrast diagram

You may find important comparisons and contrasts within one poem. Or you can compare and contrast two poems by the same poet, or two poems by different poets on the same topic. Think about similarities and differences to build your understanding of how poems work.

Differences	Similarities	Differences
Poem: Title and Author		**Poem: Title and author**
What is unique in this poem?	Do the poems share a topic?	What is unique in this poem?
Mood	What else is shared?	Mood
Idea		Idea
Use of language		Use of language

Prepare for the Reading Selections

Gaining knowledge

The pages that follow contain five poems by five poets.

Alexander L. Posey (1873–1908) was a poet, an editor, and an activist in Indian affairs. He was raised and educated in Oklahoma, known at the time as Indian Territory. Posey was of Chickasaw-Creek ancestry and did not become fluent in English, the language in which he wrote, until he was a teenager.

William Cullen Bryant (1794–1878) was an American poet and an influential newspaper editor and literary critic. The poem you will read is in a traditional form called a sonnet, which has 14 lines. The rhythm of the poem comes partly from the pattern of rhyming words at the ends of the lines.

H.D. was the pen name of Hilda Doolittle (1886–1961), an American poet who, after attending college in Pennsylvania, lived in Europe. She was a member of a group of poets called Imagists, and her poetry is known for its sharp focus on images and scenes.

Theodore Roethke [RET-kee] (1908–1963) was an American poet and college teacher. Roethke's poetry won many prestigious awards. His poems are noted for their sharp and detailed descriptions of nature.

Hamlin Garland (1860–1940) was an American short-story writer, novelist, and poet. He grew up on farms in the Midwest, and wrote realistically about prairie life.

Learn Vocabulary

Understanding vocabulary

The boxed words below are **boldfaced** in the selections. Learn the meaning of each word. Then write the word that could replace the underlined word or words in the sentence.

premature
waft
unheeded
smitten
maize
firmament
tatters
quavering
ecstatic

1. The trilling songs of birds awakened us. _____

2. The winners were overjoyed. _____

3. Fields were planted with corn. _____

4. Snow would be too early in October. _____

5. My shirt came out of the washing machine in shreds. _____

6. The beaten army retreated. _____

7. Who can count the stars in the heavens? _____

8. Pleasing smells always drift from the kitchen. _____

9. The warnings were ignored. _____

Reading Selections—Part One

Read the poems "July" by Alexander L. Posey, and "Sonnet—Midsummer" by William Cullen Bryant.

July

The air without has taken fever;
Fast I feel the beating of its pulse.
The leaves are twisted on the maple,
In the corn the autumn's **premature**;
The weary butterfly hangs waiting
For a breath to **waft** him thither at
The touch, but falls, like truth **unheeded**,
Into dust-blown grass and hollyhocks.

The air without is blinding dusty;
Cool I feel the breezes blow; I see
The sunlight, crowded on the porch, grow
Smaller till absorbed in shadow; and
The far blue hills are changed to gray, and
Twilight lingers in the woods between;
And now I hear the shower dancing
In the cornfield and the thirsty grass.

Alexander L. Posey

Sonnet—Midsummer

A Power is on the earth and in the air,
 From which the vital spirit shrinks afraid,
 And shelters him, in nooks of deepest shade,
From the hot steam and from the fiery glare.
Look forth upon the earth—her thousand plants
 Are **smitten**, even the dark sun-loving **maize**
 Faints in the field beneath the torrid blaze;
The herd beside the shaded fountain pants;
For life is driven from all the landscape brown;
 The bird has sought his tree, the snake his den,
 The trout floats dead in the hot stream, and men
Drop by the sun-stroke in the populous town;
 As if the Day of Fire had dawned and sent
 Its deadly breath into the **firmament**.

William Cullen Bryant

Completing a compare-contrast diagram

Think about how these poems are alike and different. Add your own ideas to those in the diagram below.

Differences	Similarities	Differences
Poem: "July" **by Alexander L. Posey**		**Poem: "Sonnet—Midsummer"** **by William Cullen Bryant**
poet uses "I"—seems to be in the scene	topic—summer heat	sense of death and destruction
hot air compared to feverish person with fast-beating pulse	feeling of weakness	no relief from "fiery" power
	lack of movement	
	suffering of plants and other living things	

Reading Selections—Part Two

Read the three poems that follow.

Heat

O wind, rend open the heat,
cut apart the heat,
rend it to **tatters**.

Fruit cannot drop
through this thick air—
fruit cannot fall into heat
that presses up and blunts
the points of pears
and rounds the grapes.

Cut through the heat—
plow through it,
turning it on either side
of your path.

H.D.

The Waking

I strolled across
An open field;
The sun was out;
Heat was happy.

This way! This way!
The wren's throat shimmered,
Either to other,
The blossoms sang.

The stones sang,
The little ones did,
And flowers jumped
Like small goats.

A ragged fringe
Of daisies waved;
I wasn't alone
In a grove of apples.

Far in the wood
A nestling sighed;
The dew loosened
Its morning smells.

I came where the river
Ran over stones:
My ears knew
An early joy.

And all the waters
Of all the streams
Sang in my veins
That summer day.

Theodore Roethke

In August

From the great trees the locusts cry
In **quavering ecstatic** duo—a boy
Shouts a wild call—a mourning dove
In the blue distance sobs—the wind
Wanders by, heavy with odors
Of corn and wheat and melon vines;
The trees tremble with delirious joy as the breeze
Greets them, one by one—now the oak,
Now the great sycamore, now the elm.

And the locusts in brazen chorus, cry
Like stricken things, and the ring-dove's note
Sobs on in the dim distance.

Hamlin Garland

Using a compare-contrast diagram

Choose two of the three poems in the second part of this lesson. Think about their similarities. Think about what makes each one unique. Jot down your ideas in a compare-contrast diagram.

Differences	**Similarities**	**Differences**

Check Your Understanding

Think about what you have read. Then answer these questions.

1. In the poem "July," what contrast is shown between the first and second stanzas?
   - Ⓐ heat and fever
   - Ⓑ summer air and winter wind
   - Ⓒ hot, still air and cool breezes
   - Ⓓ blinding dust and sunlight

2. What is a similarity between "Sonnet—Midsummer" and "In August"?
   - Ⓐ The poems have end rhymes.
   - Ⓑ The poems convey a mood of fear and alarm.
   - Ⓒ Words that appeal to the sense of hearing are used.
   - Ⓓ Plants are described as if they have human feelings.

3. The poem "July" has this line: "In the corn the autumn's premature." What is the likeliest meaning of that line?
   - Ⓐ The corn is dry and has stopped growing.
   - Ⓑ In the cornfields, it is not yet autumn.
   - Ⓒ The corn is ripe early in the season.
   - Ⓓ In this strange year, autumn comes in July.

4. Look back to find the word *smitten* in "Sonnet—Midsummer." Why might the poet have chosen that particular word?
   - Ⓐ to convey a feeling of love
   - Ⓑ to suggest a powerful force striking
   - Ⓒ to describe a fiery blaze
   - Ⓓ to show the connection between plants and the earth

5. In "Sonnet—Midsummer," what other phrase has a meaning similar to "deadly breath into the firmament"?
   - Ⓐ "nooks of deepest shade"
   - Ⓑ "torrid blaze"
   - Ⓒ "all the landscape brown"
   - Ⓓ "floats dead in the hot stream"

6. In the first line of the poem "Heat," what does *rend* mean?
   - Ⓐ "rip"
   - Ⓑ "enrage"
   - Ⓒ "raise"
   - Ⓓ "circle"

7. In the poem "Heat," the pears and grapes "cannot drop," because
   - Ⓐ they will not ripen in this heat.
   - Ⓑ the heat is pushing them upward.
   - Ⓒ there is no wind.
   - Ⓓ it is as if they feel they would be burned if they fell.

8. To whom is the poet talking in "Heat"?
   - Ⓐ the reader
   - Ⓑ the fruit trees
   - Ⓒ the wind
   - Ⓓ the heat

9. What is the general mood of the poem "The Waking"?
   - Ⓐ silliness
   - Ⓑ loneliness
   - Ⓒ hope
   - Ⓓ celebration

10. In "The Waking," what does the poet compare flowers to?
    - Ⓐ a wren's shimmering throat
    - Ⓑ singing blossoms
    - Ⓒ small goats
    - Ⓓ a grove of apples

11. In the poem "In August," what does the poet contrast with the "delirious joy" of the trees?

    Ⓐ distant sobs of doves

    Ⓑ a boy's wild call

    Ⓒ the oak, the sycamore, the elm

    Ⓓ the odors carried by the wind

12. Which poem seems to convey the message, "I feel connected to the whole earth"?

    Ⓐ "In August" by Hamlin Garland

    Ⓑ "The Waking" by Theodore Roethke

    Ⓒ "Heat" by H.D.

    Ⓓ "Sonnet—Midsummer" by William Cullen Bryant

Extend Your Learning

- *Write an Outdoor Poem*

   What is it like outdoors today? Step outside. Look for details. Listen carefully. Breathe deeply. Write a poem to express your sensory experience of today's weather.

- *Participate in Partner Poetry*

   With a partner, find a poetry anthology recommended by your teacher or librarian. Look for the organizing principle in the anthology—poems may be arranged by topic, theme, or poet, for example. Choose two poems that are alike in at least one way. Read the poems aloud to each other. Then take turns naming or listing the contrasts between them.

- *List Topic Pairs*

   Make a list of topic pairs—two people or characters, life forms, places, things, or ideas that are alike in some ways and different in others. The following categories are broad, but may lead you to specific topic pairs that interest you: a favorite author's works, popular music, before and after, friends, sports.

   After you have chosen your topic pairs, show similarities and differences in a compare-contrast diagram. Then use your diagram to write one or two paragraphs about how your topics are alike and different.

Making Predictions

Learn About Making Predictions

*Thinking about
the strategy*

If you are like most TV and movie viewers, you make guesses about how the story you're watching will turn out. Making guesses about future events is called **predicting**. If you are watching a mystery, you might predict who has committed the crime. If you are watching a comedy, you might predict how a ridiculous plan will backfire. Making predictions is part of the pleasure of viewing a story because predicting keeps you involved and interested. You want to find out if your prediction is right.

Making predictions is also part of the pleasure of reading a story. As you read, ask yourself:

- What do I know about the characters so far? Is a character likely to behave selfishly? generously? foolishly? cleverly?

- What do I know about this kind of story? Is it a mystery with details that might be clues? Is it an adventure story in which I can predict likely dangers to come? a legend in which great strength or heroism will probably be shown? a realistic story in which characters will act like people I know?

As you continue to read, you should check your predictions. Change your predictions or make new ones as you learn new information about the characters and events.

Studying a model

Read this opening to a story and the notes beside it.

This is a legend, so the characters might be good or evil instead of realistic. Yu Shin has a good heart and kindness.

*Prediction:
Yu Shin will continue to be obedient. But his family will continue to be cruel.*

Long, long ago in China, a boy named Yu Shin grew up with a good heart. Despite his kindness to everyone, Yu Shin was harshly treated by his parents, who favored Yu Shin's spoiled and selfish brother. One day, after Yu Shin was punished for doing nothing wrong, he went to the house of his teacher, an elderly man who was Yu Shin's only source of comfort. "How is it that parents may give special foods and favors to one son yet to the other son give only crumbs and cruelty?" Yu Shin asked.

"There is no answer to that question," replied Yu Shin's teacher. "But, as Confucius wisely teaches, you must remain obedient to your parents. Do not envy your brother. Your goodness will help you rise above any evil that surrounds you now. Be unafraid."

Yu Shin bowed and accepted his teacher's advice. He returned home, determined to accept whatever would happen without complaint.

Learn About a Graphic Organizer

When you come to a point in a story where you feel ready to make a prediction, pause to think about your ideas. Jot down the details and story knowledge that suggest events to come. Then write your prediction.

You can organize your notes in a **prediction chart** like this one. It has been filled out with information from the story opening on page 54.

What I Know So Far
Chinese legend good or evil characters Yu Shin —good, kind, obedient teacher tells Yu Shin to rise above evil family members
Prediction: Yu Shin's goodness will make him a hero.

Remember that even logical predictions are not necessarily accurate. Expect to change your predictions as you continue to read and learn new information.

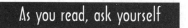
As you read, ask yourself

- What do I know about this kind of story?
- What details are clues to events to come?

Learn About a Form of Writing

A **folktale** is a kind of traditional tale, a story that is part of a people's traditions. A folktale was passed down orally from storyteller to storyteller before it was put in writing.

Folktales tend to reveal the cultures of the folk—the common people—who told them. Folktales are likely to show heroes and heroines with qualities that are valued in that culture: bravery, independence, obedience, cleverness, or strength, for example. Fools who turn out to be wise, tricksters who are too clever for their own good, and easily fooled giants are just a few of the characters commonly found in folktales.

The characters in folktales are almost never developed with realistic feelings and motives; instead, they are easily recognized "types." Knowing about the types helps you make predictions about story events. If a folktale begins with a cruel stepmother, for example, you know that the mistreated stepchild will win in the end. If a folktale introduces Coyote eyeing a meal that another animal is enjoying, you know that Coyote has a tricky plan in mind.

By taking note of character types and common patterns in a folktale, you can predict likely events. To see how to do it, read only the "What I Know So Far" section of the chart below. Try to make a prediction based on the listed details. Then read the prediction in the chart. How similar was your prediction?

What I Know So Far
Russian folktale rich and greedy merchant three aging beggars are turned away by the merchant the beggars are really holy men
Prediction: The merchant is due for heavenly punishment.

Prepare for the Reading Selection

Gaining knowledge

The pages that follow contain a retelling of a Norse, or Scandinavian, folktale. Norse tales were first collected and written down in the mid-1800s.

This tale features a setting and events that are, of course, imaginary. But the tasks shown in this story would have been familiar in Europe before the age of factories and mass-produced clothing. To make an article of clothing, someone in a household (usually a woman) first made yarn by spinning fibers on a spinning wheel. Once the yarn was spun, it was woven into fabric on a loom. Finally, the fabric was cut and stitched by hand to make an article of clothing. Spinning, weaving, and sewing all required special training.

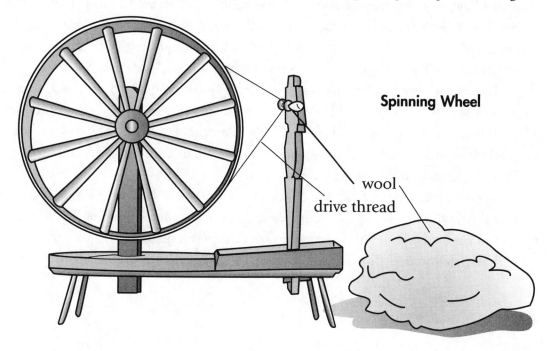

Spinning Wheel

wool
drive thread

Learn Vocabulary

Understanding vocabulary

The boxed words below are **boldfaced** in the selection. Learn the meaning of each word. Then write the word beside its definition.

provoked	
flax	
ails	
linen	
exquisite	
ells	
loathsome	
misshapen	

_____ 1. a light-colored fiber made from plant stems

_____ 2. a strong, smooth fabric

_____ 3. finely made

_____ 4. disgusting

_____ 5. stirred to action

_____ 6. formed badly

_____ 7. measures of length, each equal to the distance from the elbow to the tip of the middle finger

_____ 8. has pain or feels ill

Read the first part of the folktale "The Three Aunts."

The Three Aunts

Once, long ago, a poor man whose wife had died was left with a lovely daughter. When the daughter was nearly grown, she decided to go out in the world to try to earn her way, and her father gave her his blessing.

The girl came to a palace, asked for work, and was given a job as a maid. Soon, the queen noticed the pleasing manner and attractive appearance of the newcomer, and often complimented her. The queen's special attentions **provoked** envy in the other maids. They knew how highly the queen valued skillful housekeeping, so they told the queen that the girl had an unusual talent. They said that the girl could spin a pound of **flax** in a day and a night.

The queen, delighted, asked the girl to do the job. The girl had never spun flax in her life. But she said only, "Well, give me a room with a spinning wheel and flax, and I will try."

When she was in the room alone, the girl stared at the wheel. She did not know how it was used, or even how to begin. She began to weep. All at once, an old woman came to her. "What **ails** you, child?" asked the old woman.

Between sobs, the girl explained that she did not know how to spin flax, much less do it in a day and a night. The old woman offered to help, with one condition: "If you promise to call me Auntie on the happiest day of your life, I'll spin this flax for you."

The girl promised. The old woman said, "Just go to sleep, and leave the job to me."

The girl slept, and when she awoke, she was alone in the room. All the flax lay on the table, spun into fine and even yarn. When the queen saw it, she was mightily impressed.

Then the envious maids told the queen that the girl had boasted of being able to weave the yarn in a day and a night. The queen asked the girl to do it. Again, the girl was afraid to say no, but just asked for a room with a loom.

The girl's eyes filled with tears at the sight of the yarn and the loom. She had never even seen someone work at a loom. How could she figure out how to do it? Suddenly, another old woman appeared. "What ails you, child?" she asked.

The girl told the old woman what the queen had demanded. "If you call me Auntie on the happiest day of your life, I'll weave the yarn for you," said the old woman. The girl promised. "Then you may be off, and lie down to sleep," said the old woman.

Completing a prediction chart

Think about the first part of the folktale. Add details and predictions to the chart.

What I Know So Far
Norse folktale
poor daughter with lovely appearance and qualities
two impossible tasks solved by two old women
Predictions: There will probably be a third task.

Reading Selection—Part Two

Read the second part of the folktale "The Three Aunts."

When the girl awoke, the old woman was gone. On the table lay a piece of **linen**, woven as neatly and closely as any cloth could be. The girl delivered the linen to the queen, who smiled with great pleasure at the woven fabric and at the girl.

The other maids' envy grew even greater. Soon the queen came to the girl again: "I've been told that you are able to sew the linen into a shirt in a day and a night."

Once again, the girl dared not say she couldn't do it, so she simply asked for a room to sew in. There she waited hopefully until another old woman entered. Once again, the girl promised that on the happiest day of her life, she would call the old woman Auntie.

The next morning, when she awoke, she found the piece of linen sewn into a beautiful shirt. She brought it to the queen, who clapped at the sight of it and said, "I have never seen such **exquisite** sewing in all my born days!"

Soon after, the queen told the girl, "I have grown as fond of you as if you were my daughter. If you would like to have the prince for your husband, you can become my daughter-in-law. And you will never need to hire workwomen, for you can sew and spin and weave everything you need all by yourself."

The prince was happy with the arrangement, and soon the wedding day arrived. Just as the prince was about to sit down to the feast with his new bride, an old and very ugly woman entered the hall. The woman's nose looked three **ells** long! The bride immediately stood up, curtseyed to the woman, and said, "Good day, Auntie."

The prince could not help staring. How **loathsome** the woman looked! Could she really be his bride's aunt?

Using a prediction chart Think about what has happened since your last predictions. Write details and new predictions. Then read on to check your predictions.

What I Know So Far
Predictions:

Soon after, a second old woman entered. Her back was as wide as a door and so **misshapen** that she could not even lift her head. The bride stood quickly, curtseyed, and said, "Welcome to our happy celebration, Auntie."

The prince swallowed hard.

The third old woman had the oddest appearance of all. Her eyes were enormous and so red that it was hard to look at them without crying. "Welcome, Auntie," the bride said politely.

The prince watched the three aunts enjoying the feast. He could not contain himself. "Dear wife," he said to the girl, "how is it that someone as beautiful as you has aunts who are so . . . so . . . strange-looking?"

Each old woman answered him in turn. "I was once just as beautiful as your bride," said the long-nosed woman. "But my nose sometimes got caught in the spinning wheel while I worked week after week, and over time it stretched to this size."

The second old woman said, "I used to be straight and strong, but working my shoulders so hard at my loom day and night has turned my back into what you see now."

The third old woman said, "Once, my eyes were so lovely they could melt men's hearts. But all the close sewing I've done over the years has caused my eyes to turn red and swollen all the time."

The prince spoke. "If such work can turn beauty into ugliness, there will be no more such work for my beautiful bride. Never again shall she sew or weave or spin."

And that's the way it was.

Check Your Understanding

Think about what you've read. Then answer these questions.

1. Which of these details helps readers predict that the girl will be rewarded?
   - Ⓐ The girl is beautiful and obedient.
   - Ⓑ The other maids are envious.
   - Ⓒ The three strange women are old.
   - Ⓓ The prince is surprised.

2. Which common folktale feature helps readers predict events in this folktale?
   - Ⓐ Evil is punished.
   - Ⓑ A child is motherless.
   - Ⓒ A prince needs a wife.
   - Ⓓ Things happen in threes.

3. What does the flax become?
   - Ⓐ a plant
   - Ⓑ a spinning wheel
   - Ⓒ linen
   - Ⓓ yarn

4. What are the other maids in the palace provoked to do?
   - Ⓐ admire the prince
   - Ⓑ lie
   - Ⓒ fight
   - Ⓓ work hard

5. The queen calls the sewing exquisite. What does the word *exquisite* mean?
   - Ⓐ "superb"
   - Ⓑ "loathsome"
   - Ⓒ "smooth"
   - Ⓓ "done quickly and well"

6. Why does the girl ask for a room and a loom?
   - Ⓐ She is afraid to say no to the queen.
   - Ⓑ She knows she can figure out how to weave.
   - Ⓒ She imagines that someone will help her.
   - Ⓓ She does not know how hard spinning is.

7. What does the girl do while each old woman works?
   - Ⓐ watches and learns
   - Ⓑ spins, weaves, and sews
   - Ⓒ sleeps
   - Ⓓ cries

8. When the prince sees the second old woman, he swallows hard. Why?
   - Ⓐ Her nose is enormous.
   - Ⓑ He hears his bride call her Auntie.
   - Ⓒ The food tastes bad.
   - Ⓓ He has learned that beauty can turn to ugliness.

9. How can you tell that the girl has goodness?
   - Ⓐ She leaves home to find work.
   - Ⓑ She keeps her promises.
   - Ⓒ She speaks out against an unfairness.
   - Ⓓ She doesn't admit she cannot spin, weave, or sew.

10. Why do the three aunts come to the wedding feast?
    - Ⓐ to help the girl again
    - Ⓑ to test the prince's love
    - Ⓒ to spin, weave, and sew
    - Ⓓ to stop the marriage

11. How will the queen probably feel when she learns of her son's decision?

Ⓐ thrilled

Ⓑ envious

Ⓒ hopeful

Ⓓ disappointed

12. What was the most likely reason this folktale was told?

Ⓐ to teach the importance of learning how to spin and weave

Ⓑ to share religious beliefs

Ⓒ to explain the natural world

Ⓓ to amuse listeners

Extend Your Learning

- *Write Your Own Folktale*

  Three aunts, three daughters, three brothers, three wishes, three tasks—these are some of the trios that are commonly found in traditional tales. Think of a trio of characters, events, or things that you can put in your own original tale. Draft and revise your tale until it sounds just like a folktale.

- *Perform "The Three Aunts"*

  With other group members, prepare a script for a dramatic reading of "The Three Aunts." Distribute the speaking parts: Narrators, Girl, Queen, Aunt 1, Aunt 2, Aunt 3, Prince. Practice until the reading is smooth and expressive. Then perform for an audience.

- *Compare and Contrast*

  Find a retelling of the folktale "Rumpelstiltskin." If you do not know the story already, jot down predictions as you read it. If you do know the story, reread it and jot down clues that help readers make predictions about events to come and the story outcome. Then think about how "Rumpelstiltskin" and "The Three Aunts" are alike and different. Write a few sentences to answer this question: If a reader knew just "Rumpelstiltskin" or just "The Three Aunts," how accurately would the reader be able to predict events in the other story?

Finding Word Meaning in Context

Learn About Finding Word Meaning in Context

Thinking about the strategy

Suppose that you are reading a story and come upon this sentence:
The steady noise grew ever louder, and at last we came upon a great cataract.

What should you do if you don't know what a "great cataract" is? First, think about what you do know from the sentence—a great cataract makes a steady, loud noise. Then read on for more clues: *The waters plunged from the high cliff and crashed furiously on the rocks below.* Now can you tell what a cataract is? (a waterfall)

Whenever you come across an unfamiliar word, keep reading. You may find helpful details in the **context**—the surrounding words and sentences. Sometimes you can make a logical guess about meaning by using the general sense of the sentences, as in the example above. Other kinds of **context clues** are shown in the chart below.

Context Clues	Example Sentences	Word Meanings
definition	The Spanish word for "table," *mesa,* is the name for these flat-topped hills.	*mesa:* "flat-topped hill"
synonym (word with similar meaning)	Each difficult task was followed by an even more *arduous* one.	*arduous:* difficult
contrast word (such as but or although) and antonym	Most birds of prey are active during the day, but owls are *nocturnal* hunters.	The opposite of day is night; *nocturnal:* "occurring at night"
list that gives examples or suggests categories	The travelers became used to *privations*— sleeping on the hard ground, eating berries, and huddling under blankets in the chilly air.	*privations:* lack of comforts

Studying a model

Read the paragraph and the notes beside it.

significant— "important," "major" (general sense)

cessions—"land handed over" (example, California; and general sense)

hazards—"dangers" (synonym dangerous)

parties—"groups" (general sense)

despair—"hopelessness" (antonym hope)

Two significant events changed California history in 1848: One was the discovery of gold. The other was Mexico's land cessions, including California, to the United States. By the end of 1849, more than 80,000 newcomers had arrived in California, and more were on the way. They called themselves emigrants, and almost all were dreaming of gold. Many from the east coast took a dangerous eight-month water route, all the way around the tip of South America. Those starting out from the Midwest chose an overland route, which was also filled with hazards. The emigrants traveled in parties, most in wagon trains, and followed guide books that told them how to cross the plains, rivers, mountains, and desert. As food and water ran out, and as disease, danger, and death remained constant companions, the emigrants' hope often turned to despair.

Learn About a Graphic Organizer

A special kind of drawing, or diagram, can show how word meaning is connected to context. You can use a **definition diagram** to jot down notes about an unfamiliar word.

The diagram below shows notes about the word *emigrants*, which appears in the paragraph on page 64.

Follow these steps to fill out the diagram:

1. Write the unknown word.

2. Think about the topic. What is the author telling about in the paragraph or the passage? Jot down an idea or two.

3. Find and jot down words and phrases that are context clues—a definition, a synonym, a contrast and antonym, examples or categories, or clues that give a general sense of the sentences.

4. Write a likely meaning based on the topic and the clues.

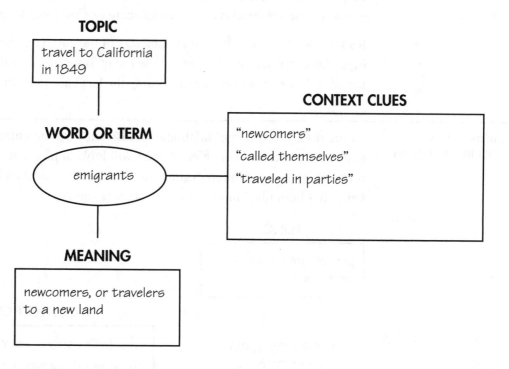

TOPIC

travel to California
in 1849

WORD OR TERM

emigrants

CONTEXT CLUES

"newcomers"

"called themselves"

"traveled in parties"

MEANING

newcomers, or travelers
to a new land

If your definition doesn't seem to match later information in the passage—and if you need to know the word in order to understand the passage—use a dictionary to determine the correct the definition.

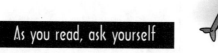
As you read, ask yourself

• What context clues can I find?

• Why is this word important to what I am reading?

Learn About a Form of Writing

Focusing on a journal

A **journal**, also called a diary, is a form of nonfiction writing. The author starts each entry with a date, and records what he or she experienced during the time since the last dated entry. People keep journals for many reasons: to make a written record of events that might otherwise be forgotten; to organize and clarify their thoughts by putting them in writing; or to express their opinions and feelings privately.

For history researchers, journals are valuable sources of information. Journals are examples of writings known as primary sources. Other primary sources include letters, interviews, and autobiographies. Most of human history occurred before there were audio recordings and cameras, but the past can still be heard and seen through primary sources.

When you read excerpts from primary sources, you may find a series of periods. These punctuation marks (. . .) are called points of ellipsis. An ellipsis stands for missing text, which has usually been left out for reasons of space or interest. You may also find words in brackets. Brackets enclose explanations that are not part of the original text.

Because journals show the written language of the past, you will find words and expressions that are not in common use today. You can still make sense of the author's meaning, however, and even enjoy letting the language pull you back to the past.

Organizing ideas in a definition diagram

As you read, you will find unfamiliar words. Some will be unfamiliar because you have never seen or heard them before. Others will look familiar but will have an unfamiliar meaning. Make a definition diagram to think about context and meaning. The diagram below has been filled in for the term "primary sources."

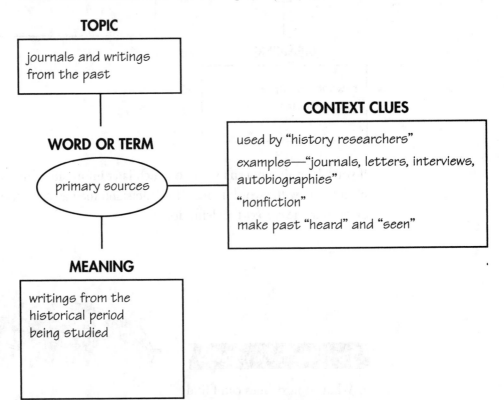

TOPIC

journals and writings from the past

WORD OR TERM

primary sources

CONTEXT CLUES

used by "history researchers"

examples—"journals, letters, interviews, autobiographies"

"nonfiction"

make past "heard" and "seen"

MEANING

writings from the historical period being studied

Prepare for the Reading Selection

Gaining knowledge

The pages that follow contain excerpts from a journal written in 1850. Margaret Frink wrote entries in the journal as she traveled overland from Indiana to Sacramento, California, from March 30 through September 7, 1850.

Margaret Frink was 32 when she made the journey with a small group under the leadership of her husband, Ledyard. (She calls her husband Mr. Frink in her journal.) She was born in Maryland, married in Kentucky, and had been living in Martinsville, Indiana, when she and Ledyard set out enthusiastically for the gold fields of California.

The Frinks made it to California, living first in Sacramento and later in Oakland. Margaret's journal was published by her husband in 1897, four years after her death. In his introduction, he said that he was publishing the book because of "the many requests made by relatives and friends for a history of our journey across the plains to California." Now, more than 100 years after its publication, and more than 150 years after it was written, the journal still conveys the adventurous spirit and sharp observations of its author.

Learn Vocabulary

Understanding vocabulary

The boxed words below are **boldfaced** in the selection. Learn the meaning of each word. Then write the word beside its definition.

emigration	1. lonely, lifeless, and sad
teams	2. to see that something is different
quicksand	3. slow-moving water that is often muddy or marshy
rumor	4. information that may or may not be true, usually spread by word of mouth
distinguish	5. two or more groups of animals harnessed together for pulling
alkali	6. a terrible smell
desolate	7. movement of people to a new settlement
bayou	8. a soft, moving mass of earth that can swallow an object on its surface
abandoned	9. mineral salts common in waters of dry lands
stench	10. left alone or unprotected

Read the first excerpts from the "Journal of the Adventures of a Party of California Gold-Seekers" by Margaret Frink.

Journal of the Adventures of a Party of California Gold-Seekers

Monday, May 20 . . . Here the two roads met. Both roads were thickly crowded with emigrants. It was a grand spectacle when we came, for the first time, in view of the vast **emigration**, slowly winding its way westward over the broad plain.

The country was so level that we could see the long trains of white-topped wagons for many miles. Finally, when the two roads came together, and the army which had crossed the Missouri River at St. Joseph joined our army, which had crossed the river above Savannah [a town north of St. Joseph, Missouri], it appeared to me that none of the population had been left behind. It seemed to me that I had never seen so many human beings in all my life before. And, when we drew nearer to the vast multitude, and saw them in all manner of vehicles and conveyances, on horseback and on foot, all eagerly driving and hurrying forward, I thought, in my excitement, that if one-tenth of these **teams** and these people got ahead of us, there would be nothing left for us in California worth picking up.

Mr. Frink was not with our wagons just at this moment; he had either ridden ahead to look for grass, or was with some one behind. So I took the responsibility, and gave orders to the drivers to whip up, to drive fast and get ahead of that countless throng of wagons. But in a little while Mr. Frink appeared, and wanted to know of the drivers what they had got in such a hurry about. Already the horses were showing signs of being fretted; and Mr. Frink at once instructed the drivers that it would not do to attempt to travel at that rate of speed if we expected ever to reach California. But I was half frantic over the idea that every blade of grass for miles on each side of the road would be eaten off by the hundreds and thousands of horses, mules, and oxen ahead of us. And, worse than all, there would only be a few barrels of gold left for us when we got to California. . . .

Tuesday, May 28 . . . The stream we had reached was fearful to look at, — rushing and boiling and yellow with mud, a mile wide, and in many places of unknown depth. The bed was of **quicksand**— this was the worst difficulty. But there was no way to do but to ford it. So we started down the bank and into the raging water. . . .

Of all the excitement that I ever experienced or thought of, the crossing of that river was the greatest. A great many other wagons and people were crossing at the same time—mule teams, horse teams, ox teams, men on horseback, men wading and struggling against the quicksands and current, many of them with long poles in their hands, feeling their way. Sometimes they would be in shallow water only up to their knees; then, all at once, some unlucky one would plunge in where it was three or four feet deep.

The deafening noise and halloing that this army of people kept up, made the alarm in the river more intense. The quicksand and the uncertainty of depth of water kept all in a state of anxiety. Our horses would sometimes be in water no more than a foot deep; then, in a moment, they would go down up to their collars. On one occasion I was considerably alarmed. Several other wagons, in their haste, had crowded in ahead of us on both sides, and we were compelled to stop for several minutes. Our wagon at once began to settle in the quicksand, and it required the assistance of three or four men lifting at the wheels, to enable the horses to pull out.

Where we crossed, the river was a mile wide, and we were just three-quarters of an hour in getting over. I here date one of the happiest and most thankful moments of my life to have been when we landed safe on the north side. The danger in the crossing consisted in the continual shifting of the sandy bed, so that a safe ford to-day might be a dangerous one to-morrow.

We were now nine-hundred and thirteen miles from home.

The next excitement we met with was some day after, when the **rumor** came back from the front that the grass ahead was all burned off. What was to become of us, with nothing for our horses to eat, and we unable to go either forward or backward?

But we out-traveled this rumor in a day. We were journeying, of course, in the dark all the time, and never knew what was in store for us ahead. . . .

Completing a definition diagram

Look back to find the word *army* in the second paragraph of the journal entry for May 20. Did you notice that *army* did not seem to have its usual meaning of "soldiers trained for war"? The first definition diagram below is partly filled out to show what *army* means in the context of that entry.

Complete the diagram. Then find the word *conveyances* in that paragraph, and the word *ford* in the first paragraph of the entry for May 28. Fill out another definition diagram for each. Use another sheet of paper.

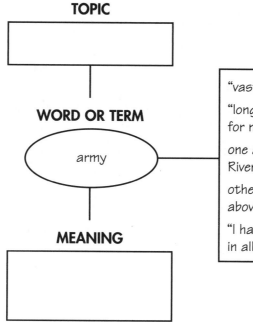

TOPIC

CONTEXT CLUES

WORD OR TERM

army

"vast emigration"

"long trains of white-topped wagons for many miles"

one army "had crossed the Missouri River at St. Joseph"

other army "had crossed the river above Savannah"

"I had never seen so many human beings in all my life before."

MEANING

Reading Selection—Part Two

Read more excerpts from the "Journal of the Adventures of a Party of California Gold-Seekers" by Margaret Frink.

Wednesday, August 14 . . . the road turned nearly south, and brought us opposite to the end or point of the mountains on our left, on the east side of the river. A broad, sandy desert opened and extended beyond them to the east and also to the south, farther than we could see. On the west, forty miles away, we could **distinguish** the long-looked-for California mountains, the Sierra Nevada, lying in a northwest and southeast direction. They were dark with heavy pine forests. On the plain was neither tree, shrub, nor blade of grass.

In a few miles we came to where the river, along which we had been traveling for the last three weeks, spreads out on the level plain, and forms a broad, shallow lake. This lake is called the "sink of the Humboldt." One-half of it sinks into the sand, the other half rises into the sky. This is the end of the most miserable river on the face of the earth. The water of the lake, as well as that of the river for the last one hundred miles above, is strong with salt and **alkali**, and has the color and taste of dirty soap-suds. It is unfit for the use of either animals or human beings; but thousands of both have had to drink it to save life.

We stopped near the margin of the sink, fed our horses from the grass in the wagon, and took dinner. . . . The total distance we have traveled thus far is two thousand one hundred fifty-eight miles.

After lunch we set forward again, and about one o'clock passed a party of emigrants who were burying a man in the sand-hills, a most **desolate** place.

Intending to travel in the night as much as we could, we drove on until eleven o'clock. Here we came to the last slough, or **bayou**, that we had to cross, and remained for the night. The water was horrible. The next morning we were to launch out in the dreadful desert, forty miles wide, with neither grass nor water on the way, and our horses ready to drop from fatigue and hunger.

Friday, August 16 . . . It was long before sunrise when we left camp. Our plan was to travel by easy stages, stopping often to feed and rest our horses. The early morning was cool and pleasant. At six o'clock we halted and rested four hours.

We set forward again at ten o'clock and soon began to realize what might be before us. For many weeks we had been accustomed to see property **abandoned** and animals dead or dying. But those scenes were here doubled and trebled. Horses, mules, and oxen, suffering from heat, thirst, and starvation, staggered along until they fell and died on every rod of the way. Both sides of the road for miles were lined with dead animals and abandoned wagons. Around them were strewed yokes, chains, harness, guns, tools, bedding, clothing, cooking-utensils, and many other articles, in utter confusion. The owners had left everything, except what provisions they could carry on their backs, and hurried on to save themselves. . . .

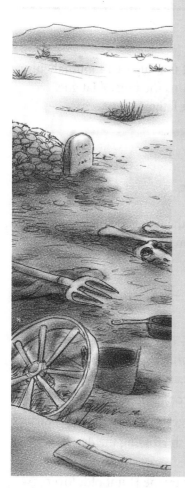

But no one stopped to gaze or to help. The living procession marched steadily onward, giving little heed to the destruction going on, in their own anxiety to reach a place of safety. In fact, the situation was so desperate that, in most cases, no one could help another. Each had all he could do to save himself and his animals.

As we advanced, the scenes became more dreadful. The heat of the day increased, and the road became heavy with deep sand. The dead animals seemed to become at every step of the way more numerous. They lay so thick on the ground that the carcasses, if placed together, would have reached across many miles of that desert. The **stench** arising was continuous and terrible.

The fault lay, in many cases, with the emigrants themselves. They acted injudiciously. Their fears caused them to drive too fast, in order to get over quickly. Their animals were too weak to be urged in this way. If the people generally had cut grass and made hay at the "big meadows" above the "sink," as Mr. Frink did, and hauled it with them into the desert, and brought a few gallons of water for each animal, traveling slowly and resting often, much of the stock and property that was lost could have been saved, and much distress and suffering avoided. . . .

It was eleven o'clock at night when we reached the river. We had been thirty-seven hours on that frightful desert. But we came through all well and without loss of animals or property. . . .

Using a definition diagram

Fill out the definition diagram below with one word that was new to you from the journal entries for August 14 or August 16. Then use another sheet of paper to fill out a definition diagram for another word from those entries.

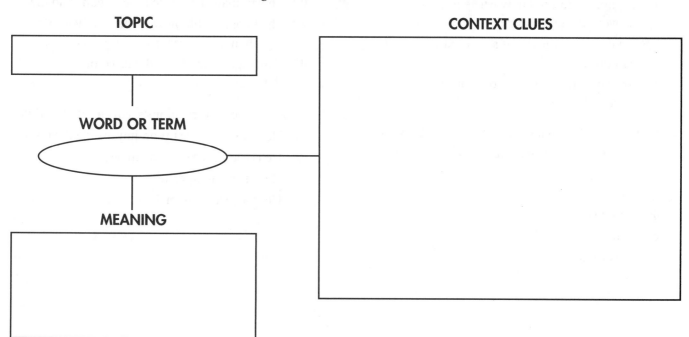

TOPIC

CONTEXT CLUES

WORD OR TERM

MEANING

Check Your Understanding

Think about what you've read. Then answer these questions.

1. Find the words "we drew nearer to the vast multitude" in the second paragraph of the journal entry for May 20. What does *multitude* mean?
   - Ⓐ "crowd"
   - Ⓑ "wagon train"
   - Ⓒ "spectacle"
   - Ⓓ "road"

2. In the journal entry for August 14, Margaret Frink writes, "We stopped near the margin of the sink. . . ." What can you picture?
   - Ⓐ a broad, treeless desert
   - Ⓑ the edge of a muddy lake
   - Ⓒ a deep river valley
   - Ⓓ abandoned and dying animals

3. What was one kind of team on the journey?
   - Ⓐ families
   - Ⓑ dogs
   - Ⓒ mules
   - Ⓓ athletes

4. The Frinks' wagon begins to settle into quicksand because
   - Ⓐ the wagon cannot move forward in the overcrowded river.
   - Ⓑ the horses do not know where to step to avoid the quicksand.
   - Ⓒ the depths of the desert sands change without warning.
   - Ⓓ three or four men have to lift at the wheels to help the horses.

5. In the next-to-last paragraph of the entry for May 28, Margaret Frink mentions a rumor. The rumor makes her feel
   - Ⓐ concerned.
   - Ⓑ responsible.
   - Ⓒ foolish.
   - Ⓓ exhausted.

6. In the last sentence of the August 14 journal entry, Margaret Frink mentions the horses' fatigue. What has caused their fatigue?
   - Ⓐ not enough food
   - Ⓑ too much effort
   - Ⓒ thirst
   - Ⓓ injuries

7. The journal includes the words below. Which word is a synonym for *desolate*?
   - Ⓐ alarmed
   - Ⓑ thankful
   - Ⓒ dangerous
   - Ⓓ miserable

8. Why does Margaret Frink's party set out long before sunrise on August 16?
   - Ⓐ The desert air is cooler then.
   - Ⓑ Their horses can get a head start on grazing.
   - Ⓒ They want to finish crossing the desert before dawn.
   - Ⓓ They want to rest by the Humboldt River at ten o'clock.

9. Many wagons lie abandoned in the desert. Why?
   - Ⓐ The wagon wheels could not roll in the sand.
   - Ⓑ The animals that pulled the wagons had died.
   - Ⓒ The people could move faster on their own legs than in the wagons.
   - Ⓓ The wagons had been damaged on the river crossing.

10. Which of these descriptions seems to fit Mr. Frink?
    - Ⓐ He refuses to give up on impossible dreams.
    - Ⓑ He is too generous sometimes.
    - Ⓒ He is short-tempered.
    - Ⓓ He is a wise planner.

11. Imagine that Margaret Frink's former neighbors in Indiana wanted to become emigrants. What advice would she probably give them?

Ⓐ Take a route that does not require crossing water or deserts.

Ⓑ Stay home—the journey is not worth any amount of gold.

Ⓒ Make sure you have enough food and water for your animals.

Ⓓ Be prepared for a grand and exciting adventure.

12. What main idea can be learned from these journal entries?

Ⓐ Emigrants to California took several routes.

Ⓑ People packed their provisions in wagons for the journey west.

Ⓒ The journey west was long, difficult, and dangerous.

Ⓓ Americans of 150 years ago were different from Americans today.

Extend Your Learning

- *Write a Journal Entry*

  Write an entry in a journal kept by a traveler. The traveler can be you, or it can be a fictional character. The entry should describe clearly what the traveler experienced. Remember to include the date.

- *Research the Emigrants' Routes*

  With your group, do research to find out how people reached California and Oregon in the mid-1800s. Make a poster-size map showing the major routes taken, and the landforms that were crossed. Illustrate the map to show vehicles, and add "Fascinating Fact" features: average length of journey, major risks, number of emigrants per year, and so on.

- *Read a Journal*

  Find published journals or other first-person accounts from the American past. Start by searching the library catalog for the Subject *United States—History—Personal Narrative*. Find a book or document that interests you. Read to share the writer's experience and views. As you read, take note of any unfamiliar words or terms that seem important to know. Use word diagrams to think about context and aid your understanding.

Drawing Conclusions and Making Inferences

Learn About Drawing Conclusions and Making Inferences

Thinking about the strategy

As you read these sentences, try to picture the character:

> "I can't believe this is happening to me!" Minerva said, sobbing.
> Tears rolled down her cheeks. "If only I had planned ahead!"

How do you think Minerva feels? What might her situation be? Now read on.

> Minerva attempted a weak smile. "I didn't think to prepare a speech,"
> she said in a choking voice. "I was sure I wouldn't win. Thank you,
> thank you, everyone, for this award. I am speechless!"

When you read the first group of sentences, did you **draw the conclusion** or **make the inference** that Minerva was upset by some terrible mistake or accident? If you did, then you were using the stated details and your own experience to think beyond the text in a reasonable way. Then, when you read on, and learned additional details, you were able to **conclude** or **infer** that Minerva was not at all upset, but overcome with happiness.

Because authors want a reader to get involved in a story, they do not state everything. Instead, they show what characters say and do, so that readers can ask themselves questions about what is happening and try to come up with likely answers. Getting involved in a story means using what is stated, along with personal experience and knowledge, to draw conclusions and make inferences.

Studying a model

Read the passage and the notes beside it.

Questions about details:

Why does Greta have blisters?

Where are Greta and Haskell?

What is Greta like? What is Haskell like?

What are the two characters trying to do?

"I'm sure we passed this tree before," said Greta. She leaned against the trunk, pulled off one sneaker, and rubbed her bare foot. "Look at these blisters!" she groaned. "Oh, why didn't I wear socks?"

"All the trees look alike," said Haskell. "I'm sure we're on the right path."

Greta gave her brother a skeptical look and pointed to a branch on the tree. "Do you see that nest? I noticed it about an hour ago, when we first passed it."

"But look at the sun!" said Haskell, pointing in the general direction of the path ahead. "It's way past noon now, so that direction must be east."

Greta sighed. "I hate to break the news to you, but the sun sets in the west, not the east. And we haven't been walking in a straight line, east or west. We've been walking in a circle."

Learn About a Graphic Organizer

Fictional stories come from the author's imagination. The author shows what the characters do, what they say, possibly what they think—and readers ask themselves questions about the characters and the events. By asking questions and trying to come up with reasonable, likely answers, readers stay engaged with the story.

Details and the conclusions or inferences they lead to can be shown in a **conclusions/inferences chart** like the one below. The examples in this chart are based on the passage on page 74.

STORY DETAILS	CONCLUSIONS/INFERENCES
Greta groans while rubbing the blisters on her foot. She says, "Oh, why didn't I wear socks?"	Greta had not expected to take such a long walk.
Greta and her brother, Haskell, are on a path with look-alike trees.	Greta and Haskell are trying to find their way through or out of the woods.
Greta noticed a bird's nest in a tree about an hour before. Now she sees the nest again.	Greta is observant. She realizes that they must have been walking in a circle.
Haskell points to the sun and the path ahead and says, "It's way past noon now, so that direction must be east."	Haskell is using the sun's position to decide that they are heading east.
Greta says that the sun sets in the west, not the east.	Haskell has been using wrong information to find the right path.

As you read, ask yourself

- What details am I reading?
- Why might the author have put in those details?
- What am I *not* being told?
- What can I figure out?

Learn About a Form of Writing

Focusing on a short story
What is a **short story**? That is not an easy question to answer, since short stories come in so many forms. Publishers generally define a short story as a work of fiction that is longer than two pages and shorter than 150 pages. The author of a short story usually has a single idea in mind.

The characters, plot, and theme are more tightly interwoven in a short story than in a longer work, such as a novel. Because every part of a short story works to create the whole, the short-story form is sometimes described as a kind of picture.

A short story is fiction—it comes from the author's imagination. Short stories may be classified as realistic fiction, mystery, horror, science fiction, and more. They may be set in the historical past, in the present, or in the future. The characters may be believable people, facing realistic problems; or the characters may be unrealistic and the events impossible. The story often has a mood or feeling—lighthearted, gloomy, suspenseful, harsh, and so on.

Short stories are found in magazines, both in print and on-line. Some periodicals are devoted to a particular category of short story—detective fiction or science fiction, for example. The shelves of the public library are filled with short-story anthologies. You can find the collected stories of an author, or anthologies arranged by topic.

Organizing ideas in a conclusions/ inferences chart
Short story writers try to make every word and sentence count. That means readers must ask themselves why particular words and sentences are included—they must draw conclusions and make inferences.

A conclusions/inferences chart like this one can help you monitor your own understanding of the details you find.

STORY DETAILS	CONCLUSIONS/INFERENCES
what characters look like, say, think, and do	unstated connections between story details
what characters say to and about one another	understandings based on personal experience
descriptions of the setting	reasonable explanations
descriptions of the action	

Prepare for the Reading Selection

Gaining knowledge
The pages that follow contain a short story. Because it involves a crime, this story might be classified as a mystery or detective story. But you will discover that the author is less concerned with the crime than with its potential for humor.

The author has chosen to tell most of the story using letters written by the characters. Some of the earliest novels ever written were **epistolary** ("having to do with letters"), and the epistolary technique is still used with novels and short stories. As you read, notice how the exchanges between the characters move the plot along as they also reveal the characters' feelings.

Learn Vocabulary

Understanding vocabulary

The boxed words below are **boldfaced** in the selection. Learn the meaning of each word. Then write the word beside its synonym or definition.

capabilities	
veranda	
tranquil	
negotiate	
perishable	
commodity	
liabilities	
assets	
ulcer	
intimated	
unequivocally	

1. _____ valuables

2. _____ inflamed sore

3. _____ destructible

4. _____ trade item

5. _____ hinted

6. _____ absolutely

7. _____ porch

8. _____ bargain

9. _____ peaceful

10. _____ means or capacities

11. _____ debts or responsibilities

Reading Selection—Part One

Read the first part of the short story "Pure Rotten" by John Lutz.

Pure Rotten

May 25, 7:00 A.M. Telephone call to Clark Forthcue, Forthcue mansion, Long Island:

"Mr. Forthcue, don't talk, listen. Telephone calls can be traced easy, letters can't be. This will be the only telephone call and it will be short. We have your stepdaughter Imogene, who will be referred to in typed correspondence as Pure Rotten, a name that fits a ten-year-old spoiled rich brat like this one. For more information check the old rusty mailbox in front of the deserted Garver farm at the end of Wood Road near your property. Check it tonight. Check it every night. Tell the police or anyone else besides your wife about this and the kid dies. We'll know. We mean business."

Click.

Buzz.

Snatchers, Inc.
May 25

Dear Mr. Forthcue:

Re our previous discussion on Pure Rotten: It will cost you exactly one million dollars for the return of the merchandise unharmed. We have researched and we know this is well within your **capabilities**. End the agony you and your wife are going through. Give us your answer by letter. We will check the Garver mailbox sometime after ten tomorrow evening. Your letter had better be there.

Sincerely,
A. Snatcher

Snatchers, Inc.
May 26

Mr. Snatcher:

Do not harm Pure Rotten. I have not contacted the authorities and do not intend to do so. Mrs. Forthcue and I will follow your instructions faithfully. But your researchers have made an error. I do not know if one million dollars is within my capabilities and it will take me some time to find out. Be assured that you have my complete cooperation in this matter. Of course if some harm should come to Pure Rotten, this cooperation would abruptly cease.

Anxiously,
Clark Forthcue

Dear Mr. Forthcue:

Come off it. We know you can come up with the million. But in the interest of that cooperation you mentioned we are willing to come down to 750,000 dollars for the return of Pure Rotten. It will be a pleasure to get this item off our hands, one way or the other.

Determinedly,
A. Snatcher

Snatchers, Inc.
May 27

Dear Mr. Snatcher:

I write this letter in the quietude of my **veranda**, where for the first time in years it is **tranquil** enough for me to think clearly, so I trust I am dealing with this matter correctly. By lowering your original figure by twenty-five percent you have shown yourselves to be reasonable men, with whom an equally reasonable man might **negotiate**. Three quarters of a million is, as I am sure you are aware, a substantial sum of money. Even one in my position does not raise that much on short notice without also raising a few eyebrows and some suspicion. Might you consider a lower sum?

Reasonably,
Clark Forthcue

Completing a conclusions/ inferences chart Draw conclusions and make inferences based on the story details so far. Fill out the missing parts of the chart.

STORY DETAILS	CONCLUSIONS/INFERENCES
	The kidnappers are running their operation like a business.
Clark Forthcue lives in a mansion. Imogene is "spoiled" and "rich."	
	A. Snatcher is very willing to bargain.
Clark Forthcue's veranda is tranquil for the first time in years.	

Read the second part of the short story "Pure Rotten" by John Lutz.

Dear Mr. Forthcue:

Pure Rotten is a **perishable** item and a great inconvenience to store. In fact, live explosives might be a more manageable **commodity** for our company to handle. In light of this we accede to your request for a lower figure by dropping our fee to 500,000 dollars delivered immediately. This is our final figure. It would be easier, in fact a pleasure, for us to dispose of this commodity and do business elsewhere.

Still determinedly,
A. Snatcher

Snatchers, Inc.
May 29

Dear Mr. Snatcher:

This latest lowering of your company's demands is further proof that I am dealing with intelligent and realistic individuals.

Of course my wife has been grieving greatly over the loss, however temporary, of Pure Rotten, though with the aid of new furs and jewelry she has recovered from similar griefs. When one marries a woman, as in acquiring a company, one must accept the **liabilities** along with the **assets**. With my rapidly improving nervous condition, and as my own initial grief and anxiety subside somewhat, I find myself at odds with my wife and of the opinion that your 500,000 dollar figure is outrageously high. Think more in terms of tens of thousands.

Regards,
Clark Forthcue

Forthcue:

Ninety thousand is *it! Final!* By midnight tomorrow in the Garver mailbox, or Pure Rotten will be disposed of. You are keeping us in an uncomfortable position and we don't like it. We are not killers, but we can be.

A. Snatcher

Snatchers, Inc.
May 30

Dear Mr. Snatcher:

Free after many years of the agonizing pain of my **ulcer**, I can think quite objectively on this matter. Though my wife demands that I pay some ransom, ninety thousand dollars is out of the question. I suggest you dispose of the commodity under discussion as you earlier **intimated** you might. After proof of this action, twenty thousand dollars will accompany my next letter in the Garver mailbox. Since I have been honest with you and have not contacted the authorities, no one, including my wife, need know of the final arrangements of our transaction.

Cordially,
Clark Forthcue

Forthcue:

Are you crazy? This is a human life. We are not killers. But you are right about one thing—no amount of money is worth more than your health. Suppose we return Pure Rotten unharmed tomorrow night? Five thousand dollars for our trouble and silence will be plenty.

A. Snatcher

Snatchers, Inc.
May 31

Dear Mr. Snatcher:

*After due reflection I must **unequivocally** reject your last suggestion and repeat my own suggestion that you dispose of the matter at hand in your own fashion. I see no need for further correspondence in this matter.*

Clark Forthcue

Snatchers Inc.
June 1

Clark Forthcue:

There has been a take over of the bord of Snatchers, Inc. and my too vise presidents who haven't got a choice agree with me, the new president. I have all the carbon copys of Snatchers, Inc. letters to you and all your letters back to us. The law is very seveer with kidnappers and even more seveer with people who want to kill kids.

But the law is not so seveer with kids, in fact will forgive them for almost anything if it is there first ofense. If you don't want these letters given to the police you will leave 500,000 dollars tomorrow night in Garvers old mailbox. I meen it. Small bils is what we want but some fiftys and hundreds will be o.k.

Sinseerly,
Pure Rotten

Using a conclusions/inferences chart

Complete a chart like the one below to show your ideas about the characters and the story details that you used as clues. Use another piece of paper.

STORY DETAILS	CONCLUSIONS/INFERENCES

Check Your Understanding

Think about what you've read. Then answer these questions.

1. What has Pure Rotten probably been doing between May 25 and June 1?
   - Ⓐ negotiating with Clark Forthcue
   - Ⓑ cooperating with Snatchers, Inc.
   - Ⓒ figuring out a way to escape
   - Ⓓ making the kidnappers miserable

2. A. Snatcher's main mistake is to
   - Ⓐ assume that Clark Forthcue wants Imogene back.
   - Ⓑ delay dropping the ransom price.
   - Ⓒ kidnap the child of parents who are not rich.
   - Ⓓ type letters, which contain clues about the crime.

3. On May 27, Clark Forthcue feels tranquil. How does he probably look?
   - Ⓐ slightly worried
   - Ⓑ relaxed and smiling
   - Ⓒ extremely anxious
   - Ⓓ exhausted

4. A. Snatcher calls Pure Rotten a commodity. What is a synonym for *commodity*?
   - Ⓐ capability
   - Ⓑ suspicion
   - Ⓒ merchandise
   - Ⓓ inconvenience

5. In the first letter on page 80, A. Snatcher says, "we accede to your request for a lower figure." What is another way of saying *accede*?
   - Ⓐ refuse
   - Ⓑ consider
   - Ⓒ offer
   - Ⓓ agree

6. On May 30, Clark Forthcue writes, "I suggest you dispose of the commodity under discussion as you earlier intimated you might." What did A. Snatcher intimate earlier?
   - Ⓐ Pure Rotten could be killed.
   - Ⓑ The authorities could be contacted.
   - Ⓒ Pure Rotten could be returned unharmed.
   - Ⓓ The fee could be lowered to ninety thousand dollars.

7. What is a main difference between Clark Forthcue and his wife?
   - Ⓐ She knows nothing about the kidnapping.
   - Ⓑ She knows more about the kidnapping than Forthcue knows.
   - Ⓒ She is even more self-centered than her husband.
   - Ⓓ She wants her daughter returned.

8. Why do the kidnappers ask for five thousand dollars when Forthcue has offered twenty thousand dollars?
   - Ⓐ They have changed their minds about the ransom.
   - Ⓑ Forthcue's money is payment for something they don't want to do.
   - Ⓒ They fear that Pure Rotten is not worth any amount of money.
   - Ⓓ Their letters cross in the mail.

9. In reply to Forthcue's letter of May 30, A. Snatcher writes that "no amount of money is worth more than your health." The likeliest reason for that statement is that
   - Ⓐ Pure Rotten has caught an illness.
   - Ⓑ Clark Forthcue has an ulcer.
   - Ⓒ A. Snatcher feels ill.
   - Ⓓ Grief over the loss of a child can cause illness.

10. What crime is Pure Rotten committing at the end?
    - Ⓐ disobedience
    - Ⓒ blackmail
    - Ⓑ kidnapping
    - Ⓓ theft

11. Why might Clark Forthcue leave 500,000 dollars in the mailbox June 2?

Ⓐ to pay the agreed-upon ransom and get Pure Rotten back

Ⓑ to avoid being arrested for attempted murder

Ⓒ to help his wife get over her grief

Ⓓ to punish the kidnappers

12. Why has the author written this short story?

Ⓐ to entertain readers with a ridiculous situation

Ⓑ to keep readers in suspense about whether the criminals will be caught

Ⓒ to show the importance of keeping children safe

Ⓓ to horrify and alarm readers

Extend Your Learning

- *Characters' Correspondence*

  Use your imagination to come up with two story characters. Write a letter that one of the characters writes to the other. Then write the other character's reply. (You may prefer to write the correspondence as postcards or e-mails.)

- *A "Pure Rotten" Performance*

  With your group, plan a performance of "Pure Rotten." Partners may share the role of the three letter writers: Clark Forthcue, A. Snatcher, and Pure Rotten. To share the role, one partner reads aloud the letter while the other silently but expressively shows the character's mood.

- *Epistolary Inferences and Conclusions*

  Epistolary novels, such as *Dear Mr. Henshaw* by Beverly Cleary, are told with letters. *Nothing But the Truth* by Avi includes letters as well as other documents. Find an epistolary work of fiction. (Start with Subject listings in the library catalog for "Letter writing—Fiction.") Or find a fictional work that includes a letter. Read the fictional letter(s) closely in order to draw conclusions and make inferences about the character and events. Show your findings in a conclusions/inferences chart.

Distinguishing Between Fact and Opinion

Learn About Distinguishing Between Fact and Opinion

Thinking about the strategy

Fiction is any kind of writing that comes from the author's imagination. Short stories and novels are examples of fiction. The kind of writing that does *not* come from the author's imagination is called *non*fiction. Nonfiction is based on **facts**. A fact is any piece of information that can be proved true. Names, dates, quantities, events, places, and similar details are facts.

You can check a fact in a reliable reference source in print or on-line. You can ask an expert. You can use your own personal knowledge and experience. All facts are true, so if you find a factual statement that is not true, you have found an error.

Although nonfiction is based on facts, it frequently includes **opinions**. Opinions tell what someone believes or feels. Opinions may express the view of the author or of people quoted by the author. Words such as *believe* and *feel*, along with descriptive words (*most important, worst, horrible, magnificent,* and so on), signal opinions.

An opinion cannot be proved true or false. But it can still make sense, especially if it is supported by facts and logic. When you find a statement of opinion, think about the facts and other reasons that support it. Decide whether you agree or disagree. Try to come up with factual, logical reasons for your opinion.

Studying a model

Read the letter and the notes beside it.

Facts:
locations of other shopping malls

location of proposed mall

effects—parking lots, widened roadways, increased accidents, lower property values

Opinions:
plans for building must be stopped

contrast between parking lots and original land

contrast between activities at a park and at a mall

To the Editor:

The plan to build a shopping mall on the Echo Bridge site in Northbud must be stopped. First of all, shoppers do not need this mall. There are already three major shopping malls within ten miles of Northbud—at Springfield, Eagleton, and Green Plains. Second, let us learn from the negative experiences of the residents of those towns. What are their experiences? They have seen vast, sun-baked parking lots replace cool green fields and woods. Their roadways have been widened to allow for increased traffic. Accidents involving cars and pedestrians have increased by 200 percent, according to police reports. Property values in the region have risen in the past three years, but in neighborhoods near the malls, home prices have dropped!

The Echo Bridge site is next to the Red River. It would make a wonderful river's edge park for the town of Northbud—a place to watch the geese and ducks, picnic under shade trees, and take a stroll. These are far more restful, worthwhile activities than fighting the traffic to visit yet another look-alike mall.

Les Noyes
Northbud Citizens Opposed to the Mall

Learn About a Graphic Organizer

Understanding a fact-opinion chart

Many kinds of nonfiction include both facts and opinions. As you read, find the statements of opinion. Think about the reasons for the opinions. Take note of any facts that are given as support.

A **fact-opinion chart** can help you separate opinion from fact. Then you can think about how convincing the author's argument seems to be.

The chart shown below is based on the letter to the editor on page 84.

OPINIONS	FACTS GIVEN IN SUPPORT
The building of the new shopping mall must be stopped. It is not needed. The landscape will be harmed. Shopping malls bring negative experiences to residents. It is more restful and worthwhile to be in a river's edge park than at a shopping mall.	There are three shopping malls within ten miles—at Springfield, Eagleton, and Green Plains. Parking lots replaced fields and woods. Roadways were widened. Accidents involving cars and pedestrians have increased by 200 percent. Property values in nearby neighborhoods have gone down. The Echo Bridge site is along the Red River.

To think about whether the author's argument is convincing, consider your own opinions and experiences. If you lived in Northbud, would you want to stop the building of the mall? Are there other facts and opinions you would want to consider before making your decision? For example, what opinions might the builder or town officials express? What kinds of supporting facts might they use?

As you read, ask yourself

- What beliefs or feelings are expressed?
- What support is given for these opinions?
- Does the support include statements that can be checked or proved?

Learn About a Form of Writing

An essay is a short nonfiction composition on a single topic. Essays are written about music, sports, movies, literature, travel, nature, people, and just about any other topic imaginable. An author chooses a topic based on personal interest. The topic might be something that has stimulated the author's curiosity or powers of observation, for example. The author might want to share humor or anger or another emotion about the topic. Regardless of the topic, the author uses the essay form to express a viewpoint.

The author's viewpoint is central in an **opinion essay,** which is sometimes called a persuasive essay. In magazines, opinion essays may be found under a heading such as "Speak Out" or "Viewpoint." In newspapers, opinion essays are often placed opposite the editorial page. The Internet is seen by many participants as a meeting place for debate, so opinion essays are everywhere on-line.

In an opinion essay, the author's main purpose is to offer convincing arguments for a viewpoint or position. The author hopes that after reading the essay, readers will say, "These opinions make sense. I agree with this author!"

Before you decide whether to be persuaded, however, you should separate the opinions from the facts. Remember that facts can be checked and proved true. Opinions cannot be proved true or false, but they can be well supported with facts and logic.

Organizing ideas in a fact-opinion chart

A fact-opinion chart can show opinions and the factual details that support them.

OPINIONS	FACTS GIVEN IN SUPPORT
Beliefs, feelings, and other statements that cannot be proved true or false. Statements that tell the reader what to think or do about an issue. Statements that can be supported with facts and convincing reasons.	Names, numbers, and other details about people, places, things, and ideas. They can be checked through research or observation. Facts are statements that can be proved true.

Prepare for the Reading Selection

Gaining knowledge

The pages that follow contain an opinion essay that includes terms having to do with hearing and sound. Sound comes from a source that vibrates. Sound energy travels from the source through air, water, or another medium. The movement of the source causes the molecules of the medium to form waves, somewhat like 3-dimensional ripples in a pond.

The number of vibrations per second is called frequency. Frequency is measured in hertz. Human ears can detect sounds with frequencies of 20 to 20,000 hertz. The higher the frequency, the higher the pitch of the sound.

Sound also has intensity, experienced as loudness. The greater the sound energy, the greater the intensity. Intensity is measured in units called decibels. Human ears can just about make out sounds at 0 decibels. A normal conversation has an intensity of about 60 decibels. And at 140 decibels, human ears feel pain rather than hear sound.

Human beings hear because of a process that begins when sound waves are captured by the outer ear. The sound waves are channeled to the eardrum, which vibrates. The middle ear has three bones that strengthen the vibrations and carry them to a connection to the inner ear. Fluid inside ducts of the inner ear's cochlea pushes against the Organ of Corti. There, tiny hair cells move and send nerve impulses to the brain.

The outer ear, middle ear, and inner ear form an amazingly effective system. But the system can be damaged. Extremely loud noises, such as from an explosion, can tear the eardrum or break the tiny bones of the middle ear. These injuries may be reversible. However, if the inner ear is damaged, partial or total hearing loss will result, and the effect is permanent.

Learn Vocabulary

Understanding vocabulary

The boxed words below are **boldfaced** in the selection. Learn the meaning of each word. Then write the word that could replace the underlined word or words in the sentence.

exposure
excessive
audiologist
inescapable
cauldrons
solace
recreation
impair
fatigue
diminished
ordinances

1. The <u>hearing specialist</u> works at a clinic. _____

2. Please obey the <u>laws</u>. _____

3. Lack of sleep may <u>weaken</u> thinking ability. _____

4. Some problems are <u>unavoidable</u>. _____

5. The child was troubled and wanted <u>comfort</u>. _____

6. Nothing <u>reduced</u> our hope. _____

7. Can eyes be harmed by <u>being subjected</u> to sunlight? _____

8. <u>Too much</u> spending is a bad habit. _____

9. Illness can cause <u>tiredness</u>. _____

10. Softball is one kind of outdoor <u>activity</u>. _____

11. What is bubbling in the <u>boiling kettles</u>? _____

Read the first part of the opinion essay "WHAT? I Can't Hear You."

WHAT? I Can't Hear You

Thump, thump, thump, booooom! The deejay just turned up the volume another notch. On the crowded dance floor, everyone is moving to the bone-jarring beat. This is a great party, isn't it? . . . Isn't it?

WHAT?

ISN'T IT? . . .

WHAT? I CAN'T HEAR YOU!

Just smile, wave, and keep dancing. There's no point in trying to talk at this kind of party. Speech cannot be heard.

It is possible that speech will never be heard again by some dancers at this party—not heard clearly, anyway. **Exposure** to the sound levels common at these events has been rated "Dangerous" or "Harmful" by the National Institute on Deafness and Other Communication Disorders. Loss of hearing ability is a result of such exposure. Sound measurements taken at loud concerts reach levels of 110 decibels and even higher. That 110-decibel level is also typically preferred by young people listening to music through headphones. The intensity is similar to what is experienced next to a chainsaw or an ambulance with the siren on. Listening to loud music is risky behavior.

Hearing loss is not the only damage that results from loud music. After attending a loud concert, for example, people often experience a ringing or humming sound in their ears. After a while, the sound goes away. But for some people, the sound *never* goes away. Musicians who play loud music are especially at risk for this distressing condition, called tinnitus. Kathy Peck is a former bass player and singer in a rock band. Her hearing loss and tinnitus led her to found an organization based in San Francisco—H.E.A.R. (Hearing Education and Awareness for Rockers). The purpose of H.E.A.R. is to educate musicians, as well as the public, to the dangers of **excessive** noise.

Certain jobs, such as musician in a loud band, pose greater risks for hearing loss and tinnitus. People who work in construction, in factories, and in mines may be exposed to noisy machinery for long periods. In 1998, the National Institute for Occupational Safety and Health updated its standards for occupational noise exposure. To prevent "occupational noise-induced hearing loss," the agency recommended an exposure limit of 85 decibels for 8 hours. If exposure is beyond that limit, workers are required to wear ear protection.

However, it is not necessary to be a rock musician or a heavy-equipment operator to be exposed to noise levels of 85 decibels and higher. In 1999, about ten million Americans with hearing loss could blame noise as the cause, at least partly. Most of those people were middle-aged or older, because the effects of noise exposure build up through time. There is evidence, however, that young people can also be harmed. Sharon Fujikawa, an **audiologist**, studied California schoolchildren's hearing. She compared results of testing in the early 1990s with results from the early 1980s. Four times as many eighth-graders in the early 1990s had high-frequency hearing loss. In New York City, free hearing tests are given at mobile clinics, sponsored by the League for the Hard of Hearing. In 1998, about 42 percent of young people tested could not hear certain 20-decibel tones. Never before had such a high percentage failed the test.

Why are so many more people of all ages showing hearing loss? The likeliest cause is increased exposure to loud noise. There is more noise now than ever before, because there are more sources than ever before.

Noise is everywhere and **inescapable**. City streets are **cauldrons** of noise. Hour after hour, city dwellers suffer from exposure to jackhammers, honking horns, screaming sirens, screeching brakes, the crash and clatter of traffic, traffic, traffic, the ceaseless rumble of air conditioners and cooling vents, the booming thunder of construction rigs, the *beep beep beep* of trucks backing up, and on and on. It is no surprise that the name given to these ear invasions is not just *noise*, but *noise pollution*.

Completing a fact-opinion chart

Read the listed opinions from the first part of the opinion essay. Write at least four facts that the author gives to support the opinions.

OPINIONS	FACTS GIVEN IN SUPPORT
Listening to loud music is risky behavior. City dwellers suffer from the ear invasions known as noise pollution.	

Read the second part of the opinion essay "WHAT? I Can't Hear You."

Noise pollution is worst in the cities. But the suburbs, which draw people out of cities in search of a more peaceful way of life, also make the noise meters jump. Suburbs exist because of highways and cars. Highways and cars mean noise, and the background roar of traffic often accompanies the backyard barbecue. Suburbanites also use noisemaking machinery to keep their property in shape: leafblowers, power mowers, hedge trimmers, chainsaws, snowblowers, and more. The expansion of the suburbs brings the noisemaking activities of construction equipment. And these are just the *outdoor* machines!

People who can't stand the noise anymore seek **solace** in the country. Perhaps somewhere in the mountains, they find a shimmering lake surrounded by forest. In it churn buzzing powerboats and the personal watercraft known as Jet Skis. It seems as if **recreation** cannot take place without noise. With motorbikes, all-terrain vehicles, snowmobiles, and vehicles yet to be invented, noise is part of the "fun." Of course, it is not fun for anyone who is searching for a quiet place to think.

Noise can make it harder to learn. A psychologist in New York City, Arline Bronzaft, studied a school that was next to the tracks of an elevated train. Every few minutes, a train clattered by, bringing 89-decibel levels of noise into the classrooms. Not all the classrooms were noisy, however. On the other side of the school, students were learning in quieter classrooms. When Bronzaft compared the results of reading tests, the noisy-classroom students scored one full year below the quiet-classroom students. Noise-reducing materials were eventually added to the tracks and the school. When the study was later repeated, there were no differences in scores between the two sides of the school.

Other studies in the United States and around the world have shown that traffic noise and aircraft noise can **impair** children's reading comprehension and the ability to memorize information.

Noise is any unwanted sound. If people are forced to listen to constant sounds that they do not want and cannot stop, they suffer from **fatigue** and headaches. A sudden burst of noise causes the body's adrenal glands to release the substances adrenaline and noradrenaline (also called epinephrine and norepinephrine) into the bloodstream. Very loud and steady noise also stimulates the release of these substances. The adrenal glands help the body respond to danger, allowing the person to be very alert and ready to fight or run. Adrenaline makes the heart pump harder and faster. Blood pressure goes up. The body produces more energy. But what if the body responds in these ways again and again, because of noise rather than real danger? Then physical health is threatened. And the person feels tense and irritable. Noise can lead to rage. It can also lead to feelings of hopelessness and depression.

The poisonous effects of noise pollution have to do with the issue of "quality of life." Everyone wants a satisfying quality of life. To understand what that means, just glance at real-estate ads. Why don't ads say, "Right next to the airport!" or "Barking dogs at every window!" The answer is obvious. Nobody would want to buy or rent if there were no chance of relaxing in an easy chair in the living room, sleeping through the night, reading a book, and doing other normal activities without disturbance or stress. The quality of life is **diminished** for people who live near a speedway, an airport, a highway, or some other source of never-ending noise. Often, they cannot afford to move. Sometimes, they form associations with neighbors to make changes.

Civic action may be the only way to reduce noise pollution. Local lawmakers can be persuaded to set noise **ordinances**. As a result, in some cities and towns, horn-honking drivers and owners of barking dogs have to pay fines. Certain recreational vehicles are banned. Operators of noisy machines may face punishment if the machines are on during "off" hours. Noise polluters of all kinds may even be arrested. Residents of neighborhoods near airports in Chicago, New York City, Boston, Seattle, and other cities have joined to fight airport expansion. Similar associations have been formed to limit the noise-making activities at speedways and outdoor arenas. These anti-noise efforts must continue if we are to protect our hearing, our health, and our quality of life.

Using a fact-opinion chart

Fill out this chart with at least two opinions from the second part of the opinion essay. Then write facts given to support those opinions.

OPINIONS	FACTS GIVEN IN SUPPORT

Check Your Understanding

Think about what you've read. Then answer these questions.

1. Which of these statements gives an opinion?
   - Ⓐ About 42 percent of young people tested could not hear 20-decibel tones.
   - Ⓑ The effects of noise exposure build up through time.
   - Ⓒ More people of all ages are showing hearing loss.
   - Ⓓ It seems as if recreation cannot take place without noise.

2. Which of these phrases from the opinion essay is factual?
   - Ⓐ "background roar of traffic"
   - Ⓑ "excessive noise"
   - Ⓒ "high-frequency hearing loss"
   - Ⓓ "booming thunder of construction rigs"

3. Why is tinnitus distressing?
   - Ⓐ It has an effect on the adrenal glands.
   - Ⓑ It is caused by hearing loss.
   - Ⓒ Musicians can prevent it by wearing ear protection.
   - Ⓓ The ringing or humming is inescapable.

4. Why does the author compare city streets to "cauldrons of noise"?
   - Ⓐ to suggest that a poisonous mixture is bubbling and brewing
   - Ⓑ to point out that noise and heat are alike
   - Ⓒ to suggest that clanging instruments are being played too loudly
   - Ⓓ to help readers imagine sudden bursts of noise

5. What is noise pollution?
   - Ⓐ background sounds that never stop
   - Ⓑ harmful, disturbing, and unwanted sounds
   - Ⓒ outdoor machinery
   - Ⓓ dust and chemicals in the air that lead to health problems

6. What was learned from the study of students in a school next to train tracks?
   - Ⓐ Do not build a school next to an elevated train.
   - Ⓑ Learning to read requires absolute quiet.
   - Ⓒ Noise can make it harder to learn to read.
   - Ⓓ Students can learn to read even when noise levels reach 89 decibels.

7. What do the adrenal glands have to do with noise?
   - Ⓐ Noise can cause the glands to release adrenaline and noradrenaline.
   - Ⓑ The purpose of the adrenal glands is to help a person respond to dangers such as noise from machinery.
   - Ⓒ Substances from the glands make a person alert to noise.
   - Ⓓ Chemical releases from the glands lead to fatigue and headaches.

8. According to the opinion essay, what are three main effects of noise?
   - Ⓐ hearing loss, solace, learning problems
   - Ⓑ recreational vehicles, machinery, loud music
   - Ⓒ hearing loss, physical illness, emotional distress
   - Ⓓ pollution, recreation, comprehension

9. With which of these opinions would the author agree most?
   - Ⓐ Beachgoers have the right to relax with music from a boom box.
   - Ⓑ Vehicles that make noise should be banned.
   - Ⓒ Neighbors who are disturbed by noise should complain.
   - Ⓓ Musicians should play only soft music.

10. The author says, "Everyone wants a satisfying quality of life." What is another way of saying that?
    - Ⓐ People wish to avoid struggling with everyday activities.
    - Ⓑ People just want to live as simply as possible.
    - Ⓒ People are basically respectful and kind.
    - Ⓓ Every human being has the same needs for living.

11. In the last paragraph of the opinion essay, the author recommends civic action. What is an example of civic action?

Ⓐ complaining in a polite and civilized manner

Ⓑ forming an armed group to attack noise polluters

Ⓒ putting noise polluters in jail

Ⓓ joining with others to influence lawmakers

12. What is the author's main purpose in this essay?

Ⓐ to persuade people to reduce noise pollution

Ⓑ to describe noisy settings

Ⓒ to explain the difference between noise and sound

Ⓓ to entertain readers with facts about the dangers of noise

Extend Your Learning

- *Draw a Political Cartoon*

  The author of the essay "WHAT? I Can't Hear You" has expressed opinions about noise pollution. Others may disagree with some of the opinions. Think about different viewpoints on the issue, including your own. Show a viewpoint in a political cartoon. For examples of political cartoons, look at the editorial pages of newspapers.

- *Research Noise Ordinances*

  With other group members, learn about the noise codes of your city or town. What kinds of noisy activities are against the law? Who is in charge of enforcing the rules? What are the punishments for lawbreakers? Print out a copy of the regulations. Write notes in everyday language to explain what the law says.

- *Find News Items*

  Use on-line databases to find a news article about a noise-related issue. Print out the article. Copy statements of opinion. Jot down facts that are given to support the opinions. Then write a statement of your own opinion on the issue.

LESSON 10
Identifying Author's Purpose

Learn About Identifying Author's Purpose

Thinking about the strategy

Consider this list of writings: a software manual, song lyrics, an advertisement, a news article about a world event, a science textbook chapter, a speech by a politician. These varied writings are written for different purposes. By thinking about an **author's purpose**, you may decide to read slowly, read faster, skim, reread, or take notes.

What is author's purpose? An author may write

- to give facts, information, ideas, or instructions. The author's general purpose is **to explain or inform**.

- to tell a true or a fictional story, to make characters seem real, to make a topic fascinating, to evoke emotions, or to share personal experiences. The author's general purpose is **to entertain**.

- to give vivid details about people, places, and things; to set a mood; to put readers "right there" in the scene. The author's general purpose is **to describe**, or **to express**.

- to give opinions and support for them, to show why an idea or a belief is right or wrong, to get readers to agree with a position or to take an action. The author's general purpose is **to persuade**.

Authors rarely have just one purpose for writing. An author who writes a science book, for example, may have the general purpose "to explain or inform," but probably also has other purposes as well—to entertain, to describe, and possibly to persuade.

Studying a model

Read the passage and the notes beside it.

Facts about Powell's life
Opinion about early influences

Colin Luther Powell was born in New York City in 1937. His parents both worked hard to support the family. Powell grew up with an important message: To succeed, get an education. The New York City public schools provided Powell with that education. He graduated from City College in 1958 with a degree in geology. He joined the United States Army that same year.

Facts about Powell's career
Opinion about leadership ability

Colin Powell served in Vietnam, Korea, and Europe. His leadership skills became apparent to his officers early on, and he rose through the ranks, all the way up to four-star general. He advised three presidents on military matters. General Powell retired from the U.S. Army in 1993. He founded America's Promise, an organization designed to guide children to successful lives.

Description of Powell's manner
Opinion about his effects
Facts about current position

A soft-spoken man with a commanding presence, Colin Powell inspired trust in Americans of differing political viewpoints. In 2001, he was nominated by newly elected President George W. Bush to be Secretary of State. His nomination was easily confirmed. Colin Powell became the first African-American to serve as the nation's most important diplomat to the world.

Learn About a Graphic Organizer

Understanding an author's purpose chart

Thinking about an author's purpose can help you understand and evaluate the writing. Ask yourself questions about what the author wrote, and why it might have been written that way. Think about the author's word choice. Build your awareness of the techniques authors use to fulfill their purposes.

Examples of questions and answers about an author's purposes are shown in the **author's purpose chart** below. The information comes from the passage on page 94.

QUESTION: Why does the author . . .	PURPOSE
give dates of birth and college graduation? tell that he attended New York City schools? tell when he joined the U.S. Army?	to inform readers of facts of Powell's life
tell that his family stressed education?	to explain why Powell values education
mention leadership skills? say that he inspired trust?	to persuade readers that Powell is especially deserving of respect
say "soft-spoken man with a commanding presence"?	to describe, helping readers picture Powell's quiet confidence

The example passage is nonfiction. The chart shows that its author's main purposes are to inform and explain. Additional purposes are to persuade and to describe.

As you read, ask yourself

- Does the author give facts or tell how to do something? The purpose may be to explain or to inform.
- Does the author include suspense, humor, lively language, intriguing information, or other features that keep readers involved and interested? The purpose may be to entertain.
- Does the author paint sharp pictures of people, places, and things? The purpose may be to describe or express.
- Does the author give opinions and supporting reasons? The purpose may be to persuade.

Learn About a Form of Writing

Focusing on a speech

If you were to look at a book of collected speeches, you might find them organized in categories. Speeches are given to honor heroic actions, to gain votes, to accept awards, to stir listeners to action, to offer congratulations, and more.

Speeches are a form of oral communication. Although they are written, they are meant to be read aloud. The speaker's voice is important in conveying meaning and feeling. An audience listening to a speech can hear the rise and fall of sentences, the words that are given extra emphasis, the emotion in the speaker's voice, and the laughter or murmurs of their fellow listeners. A reader can only imagine those things. When you read the written form of a speech, try to imagine the speaker's voice and the audience's reaction. Read aloud to yourself.

Think about what the author of the speech is trying to achieve. Is the author's general purpose to explain or inform? to entertain? to describe? to persuade? What does the author do to fulfill the main purpose and other purposes?

Organizing ideas in an author's purpose chart

An author's purpose chart can show questions about information in the speech and answers about purposes.

QUESTION: Why does the author of a speech . . .	PURPOSE
give names, dates, and other facts or details?	to explain or inform
use sharp and vivid words to tell about a scene, a person, or a thing?	to describe (or express)
offer opinions and supporting reasons? use emotionally powerful and stirring words? tell why someone's ideas are right or wrong? ask for votes or other actions?	to persuade
include a personal story? include a joke? mention members of the audience or address them directly?	to entertain

Prepare for the Reading Selection

Gaining knowledge
The pages that follow contain an excerpt from a speech given by Colin Powell at Howard University on May 14, 1994. The retired general had been invited to give the commencement address at this well-respected and predominantly African-American school. A commencement address is a speech delivered to an audience of graduating students, their families, friends, and other members of the university. A commencement address is usually given at a happy, hopeful time. But in May of 1994, there was conflict on the campus of Howard University.

The conflict had to do with the issue of free speech versus hate speech. Several weeks earlier, a speaker formerly associated with the Nation of Islam had spoken at a rally on the Howard University campus. The speech, it was reported, fired up hatred of whites, and targeted Jews. It was unclear how many Howard University students even attended the rally. But there was great tension and controversy at the time of graduation. Colin Powell faced a challenging situation. What would he say at the commencement address?

Learn Vocabulary

Understanding vocabulary

The boxed words below are **boldfaced** in the selection. Learn the meaning of each word. Then write the word beside its clue.

controversy	
platitudes	
mundane	
reconciling	
apartheid	
intractable	
legacy	
destiny	
honorees	
philanthropists	

1. Synonym for *stubborn* _____

2. Synonym for *everyday* _____

3. Synonym for *dispute* _____

4. Ending a dispute _____

5. South African policy of racial separation _____

6. "Look on the bright side" and "every cloud has a silver lining" are examples. _____

7. What one generation passes to the next _____

8. People who give generously _____

9. Medal winners, for example _____

10. This hasn't happened yet, but will. _____

Reading Selection—Part One

Read this excerpt from a speech by Colin Powell.

Commencement Address by Colin Powell, Howard University, 1994

The real challenge in being a commencement speaker is figuring out how long to speak.

The graduating students want a short speech, five to six minutes and let's get it over. They are not going to remember who their commencement speaker was anyway. P-O-W-E-L-L.

Parents are another matter. Arrayed in all their finery they have waited a long time for this day, some not sure it would ever come, and they want it to last. So go on and talk for two or three hours. We brought our lunch and want our money's worth.

The faculty member who suggested the speaker hopes the speech will be long enough to be respectable, but not so long that he has to take leave for a few weeks beginning Monday.

So the poor speaker is left figuring out what to do. My simple rule is to respond to audience reaction. If you are appreciative and applaud a lot early on, you get a nice, short speech. If you make me work for it, we're liable to be here a long time.

You know, the **controversy** over Howard's speaking policy has its positive side. It has caused the university to go through a process of self-examination, which is always a healthy thing to do.

Since many people have been giving advice about how to handle this matter, I thought I might as well too. First, I believe with all my heart that Howard must continue to serve as an institute of learning excellence where freedom of speech is strongly encouraged and rigorously protected. That is at the very essence of a great university and Howard is a great university.

And freedom of speech means permitting the widest range of views to be present for debate, however controversial those views may be.

The First Amendment right of free speech is intended to protect the controversial and even outrageous word, and not just comforting **platitudes**, too **mundane** to need protection.

Some say that by hosting controversial speakers who shock our sensibilities, Howard is in some way promoting or endorsing their message. Not at all. Howard has helped put their message in perspective while protecting their right to be heard. So that message can be exposed to the full light of day.

I have every confidence in the ability of the administration, the faculty and the students of Howard to determine who should speak on this campus. No outside help needed, thank you.

I also have complete confidence in the students of Howard to make informed, educated judgments about what they hear. But for this freedom to hear all views, you bear a burden to sort out wisdom from foolishness.

There is great wisdom in the message of self-reliance, of education, of hard work, and of the need to raise strong families.

There is utter foolishness, evil, and danger in the message of hatred, or of condoning violence, however cleverly the message is packaged or entertainingly it is presented.

We must find nothing to stand up and cheer about or applaud in a message of racial or ethnic hatred.

I was at the inauguration of President Mandela in South Africa earlier this week. You were there too by television and watched that remarkable event. Together, we saw what can happen when people stop hating and begin **reconciling**. DeKlerk the jailer became DeKlerk the liberator, and Mandela the prisoner became Mandela the president.

Twenty-seven years of imprisonment did not embitter Nelson Mandela. He invited his three jail keepers to the ceremony. He used his liberation to work his former tormentors to create a new South Africa and to eliminate the curse of **apartheid** from the face of the earth. What a glorious example! What a glorious day it was!

Last week you also saw Prime Minister Rabin and PLO Chairman Arafat sign another agreement on their still difficult, long road to peace, trying to end hundreds of years of hatred and two generations of violence. . . .

In these two historic events, **intractable** enemies of the past have shown how you can join hands to create a force of moral authority more powerful than any army and which can change the world.

Although there are still places of darkness in the world where the light of reconciliation has not penetrated, these two beacons of hope show what can be done when men and women of goodwill work together for peace and for progress.

There is a message in these two historic events for us assembled here today. As the world goes forward, we cannot start going backward.

Completing an author's purpose chart   Use what you have read so far to add information to this chart.

QUESTION: Why does Powell . . .	PURPOSE
start out by talking about the length of his speech?	to entertain and relax the audience with humor
say that controversial and even outrageous speeches should be permitted?	
	to persuade listeners of the importance of using wisdom in judging messages
talk about the recent inauguration of President Mandela in South Africa?	

Read the rest of the excerpt of Colin Powell's speech.

African-Americans have come too far and we have too far yet to go to take a detour into the swamp of hatred. We, as a people who have suffered so much from the hatred of others, must not now show tolerance for any movement or philosophy that has at its core the hatred of Jews or anyone else.

Our future lies in the philosophy of love and understanding and caring and building. Not of hatred and tearing down.

We know that. We must stand up for it and speak up for it!

We must not be silent if we would live up to the **legacy** of those who have gone before us from this campus.

I have no doubt that this controversy will pass and Howard University will emerge even stronger, even more than ever a symbol of hope, of promise, and of excellence. That is Howard's **destiny**!

Ambassador Annenberg, one of your **honorees** today, is a dear friend of mine and is one of America's leading businessmen and greatest **philanthropists**. You have heard of his recent contribution to American education and his generous gift to Howard. A few years ago I told Mr. Annenberg about a project I was involved in to build a memorial to the Buffalo Soldiers, those brave black cavalrymen of the West whose valor had long gone unrecognized. Ambassador Annenberg responded immediately, and with his help the memorial now stands proudly at Fort Leavenworth, Kansas.

The Buffalo Soldiers were formed in 1867, at the same time as Howard University. It is even said that your mascot, the bison, came from the bison, or buffalo, soldiers. Both Howard and the Buffalo Soldiers owe their early success to the dedication and faith of white military officers who served in the Civil War. In Howard's case, of course, it was your namesake, Major General Oliver Howard.

For the 10th Cavalry Buffalo Soldiers, it was Colonel Benjamin Grierson who formed and commanded that regiment for almost twenty-five years. And he fought that entire time to achieve equal status for his black comrades.

Together, Howard University and the Buffalo Soldiers showed what black Americans were capable of when given the education and opportunity; and when shown respect and when accorded dignity.

I am a direct descendant of those Buffalo Soldiers, of the Tuskegee Airmen, and of the navy's Golden Thirteen, and Montfort Point Marines, and all the black men and women who served this nation in uniform for over three hundred years.

All of whom served in their time and in their way and with whatever opportunity existed then to break down the walls of discrimination and racism to make the path easier for those of us who came after them.

I climbed on their backs and stood on their shoulders to reach the top of my chosen profession to become chairman of the American Joint Chiefs of Staff. I will never forget my debt to them and to the many white "Colonel Griersons" and "General Howards" who helped me over the thirty-five years of my life as a soldier. . . .

You face "Great Expectations." Much has been given to you and much is expected from you. You have been given a quality education, presented by a distinguished faculty who sit here today in pride of you.

You have inquiring minds and strong bodies given to you by God and by your parents, who sit behind you and pass on to you today their still unrealized dreams and ambitions.

You have been given citizenship in a country like none other on earth, with opportunities available to you like nowhere else on earth, beyond anything available to me when I sat in a place similar to this thirty-six years ago.

What will be asked of you is hard work. Nothing will be handed to you. You are entering a life of continuous study and struggle to achieve your goals. A life of searching to find that which you do well and love doing. Never stop seeking.

I want you to have faith in yourselves. I want you to believe to the depth of your soul that you can accomplish any task that you set your mind and energy to.

I want you to be proud of your heritage. Study your origins. Teach your children racial pride and draw strength and inspiration from the cultures of our forebears. Not as a way of drawing back from American society and its European roots. But as a way of showing that there are other roots as well. African and Caribbean roots that are also a source of nourishment for the American family tree.

To show that African-Americans are more than a product of our slave experience. To show that our varied backgrounds are as rich as that of any other American, not better or greater, but every bit as equal.

Our black heritage must be a foundation stone we can build on, not a place to withdraw into. I want you to fight racism. But remember, as Dr. King and Dr. Mandela have taught us, racism is a disease of the racist. Never let it become yours. . . .

Go forth to make this a better country and society. Prosper, raise strong families, remembering that all you will leave behind is your good works and your children.

Go forth with my humble congratulations. And let your dreams be your only limitations. Now and forever. Thank you and God bless you.

Have a great life!

Using an author's purpose chart   Fill out this chart with your ideas about the second part of the speech.

QUESTION: Why does Powell . . .	PURPOSE

Check Your Understanding

Think about what you've read. Then answer these questions.

1. What is a major purpose of Colin Powell's commencement address?
   Ⓐ to describe Howard University
   Ⓑ to persuade graduates to stop listening to controversial speakers
   Ⓒ to persuade listeners of the importance of tolerance
   Ⓓ to explain a historical concept

2. Reread paragraph 5 on page 98. (It begins, "So the poor speaker . . . ") What is Powell probably trying to achieve with his remark?
   Ⓐ Get the audience to loosen up and laugh.
   Ⓑ Show strong emotion.
   Ⓒ Make a persuasive point.
   Ⓓ Talk about his own achievements.

3. Why does Powell say that the recent controversy at Howard University has a positive side?
   Ⓐ It has caused Howard University students to believe in racial justice.
   Ⓑ It has caused outsiders to give attention to Howard University.
   Ⓒ It has allowed messages of hatred to disappear.
   Ⓓ It has provoked honest discussion.

4. Powell says that the First Amendment right of free speech is designed to protect more than just platitudes. What are platitudes?
   Ⓐ mild, unoriginal ideas
   Ⓑ controversial viewpoints
   Ⓒ speeches
   Ⓓ forceful attitudes

5. What does Powell think of speeches that condone violence and hatred?
   Ⓐ They deserve to be heard on a college campus.
   Ⓑ College students should not be allowed to listen to them.
   Ⓒ They are too shocking to people's sensibilities.
   Ⓓ Audiences should stand up, cheer, or applaud.

6. What does Powell hope that African-American students will do if they hear an entertaining speech that is anti-white?
   Ⓐ Appreciate the speaker's message.
   Ⓑ Reject the message.
   Ⓒ Decide whether the ideas make sense.
   Ⓓ Never invite the speaker back.

7. When Powell tells about the inauguration of Nelson Mandela, he says, "What a glorious example! What a glorious day it was!" Why does he use those phrases?
   Ⓐ to inform his listeners
   Ⓑ to describe the ceremony
   Ⓒ to persuade listeners to support Mandela
   Ⓓ to express joyful emotion

8. How does Powell describe feeling when he sees intractable enemies reconciling?
   Ⓐ disappointed
   Ⓑ hopeful
   Ⓒ tormented
   Ⓓ doubtful

9. In the first paragraph on page 100, Powell advises against taking a "detour into the swamp of hatred." Why does he use the word *swamp*?
   Ⓐ A swamp is a wet place with many insects.
   Ⓑ Swamps are hated places.
   Ⓒ It is easy to get stuck in a swamp and hard to find the way out.
   Ⓓ A swamp is a kind of road that never ends.

10. Reread paragraph 10 on page 100. (It begins, "I am a direct descendant . . . ") Who are the Tuskegee Airmen?
    Ⓐ Colin Powell's grandparents or other ancestors in the U.S. Army
    Ⓑ the first African-American military pilots
    Ⓒ black cavalrymen of the West
    Ⓓ the first African-Americans to fly planes

11. What does Powell mean when he says that the graduating students face "great expectations"?

  Ⓐ They will have to struggle to meet their goals.

  Ⓑ They have reason to hope for future success.

  Ⓒ They are now well educated.

  Ⓓ They cannot fail.

12. What is Powell's major point in the last paragraphs of his speech?

  Ⓐ Your dreams and ambitions may be unrealized.

  Ⓑ Make the fight against racism your life's work.

  Ⓒ Accept your limitations, but don't be afraid to dream.

  Ⓓ Believe in yourselves, and be proud of your heritage.

Extend Your Learning

- *Write a Speech*

  You have just won the award of your dreams! Write your acceptance speech. Be sure to tell how you feel about this award, and thank everyone who helped you. If you wish, deliver the speech to classmates.

- *Research Current Events*

  With other group members, use on-line sources to locate news articles that tell about Colin Powell and his current work. Display the articles along with summarizing paragraphs.

- *Identify Author's Purpose*

  Find a print or an audio collection of speeches. Choose one speech to analyze. Make an author's purpose chart to show the speechmaker's major purpose and additional purposes.

LESSON 11 Interpreting Figurative Language

Learn About Interpreting Figurative Language

Thinking about the strategy

Read these two sentences, and think about the different meanings of the underlined words:

1. After counting the raised hands, the teacher said, "Please put your <u>hands down</u> now."

2. The home team won the game <u>hands down</u>.

In sentence 1, the words *hands down* have their **literal** meaning—raised hands are to be lowered. In sentence 2, the literal meaning of *hands down* does not make sense. In this sentence, *hands down* means "easily" or "without working hard." An expression in which the words do not have their usual, literal meaning is called an **idiom**. In an idiom, the words have a **figurative** meaning.

Idioms are common in speech and writing, but figurative language can also be used in uncommon, original ways. Poets and other writers use **figurative comparisons** to create vivid images and emotional impact. Here are three kinds of figurative comparisons:

- In a **simile**, the comparison is made with the word *like* or *as*. Examples: *A favorite book is as comfortable as a hug.* (A favorite book is compared to a comfortable hug.) *Opening to the first page is like greeting an old friend.* (The act of opening the book is compared to greeting an old friend.)

- In a **metaphor**, the comparison is made directly, without *like* or *as*. Example: *A candle of sunlight flickered behind gray clouds.* (The sun is compared to a flickering candle.)

- In **personification**, something that is not alive is given the traits of a living thing, or something that is not human is given the traits of a person. In these examples, a ringing telephone is made lifelike: *The phone refused to stop ringing. Its high-pitched shrieks demanded attention hour after hour.*

Studying a model

Read the paragraphs and the notes beside them.

playground swing compared to living thing	The playground was empty in the midafternoon heat. I lowered my body onto a swing, which groaned in protest. I thought about swinging through the air, because it could create a breeze. But I did not have the energy or will to pump. The air felt as thick as a blanket.
air compared to thick blanket	
leaves compared to people	Then I became aware that the light had dimmed. The leaves on nearby trees began to whisper, "Rain, rain, rain." At first, the raindrops came as single hoofbeats. But within moments, the sky opened its gates, and water crashed out like a wild herd. I enjoyed a thorough soaking. Only when I heard the drums of distant thunder did I head for shelter.
raindrops compared to hoofbeats	
sky compared to living thing	
rain compared to wild herd	
thunder compared to drums	

104

Learn About a Graphic Organizer

Understanding a figurative language chart

As you read, try not only to understand what the author is saying, but also to appreciate how the author is saying it. Look for figurative comparisons. Ask yourself how you can tell that the comparison is figurative, and not literal. Think about what the comparison helps you picture or understand.

This **figurative language chart** shows the figurative comparisons from the paragraphs on page 104.

Figurative Comparison	What Is Compared	Effects of the Comparison
"... a swing, which groaned in protest." (personification)	a playground swing and a person or other living thing that protests by groaning	hear the sound of the swing; appreciate the feeling of weakness in the heat
"The air felt as thick as a blanket." (simile)	air and blanket	feel the heaviness of the heat
"The leaves on nearby trees began to whisper, 'Rain, rain, rain.'" (personification)	leaves and whispering people	imagine the slight movements of the leaves as they are stirred by the breeze that comes before rain
"...the raindrops came as single hoofbeats." (metaphor)	raindrops and hoofbeats	see the single drops and hear their beating sounds
"... the sky opened its gates, ..." (personification)	sky and person who can open gates	appreciate the suddenness and rush of the heavy rain
"... water crashed out like a wild herd." (simile)	rainfall and herd of wild animals	hear the crashing noise; experience the power of the rain
"... I heard the drums of distant thunder. ..." (metaphor)	thunder and drums	hear the sound of thunder

As you read, ask yourself

- Is the unusual comparison a simile, a metaphor, or personification?
- What unlike things are being compared?
- What effects do the figurative comparison have on me, the reader?

Learn About a Form of Writing

Focusing on a travel essay

An essay is any composition, usually brief, on a nonfiction topic. In a personal essay, the author shares thoughts and feelings about the topic, using first-person pronouns such as *I, me,* and *we*. A **travel essay** is a special kind of personal essay. In a travel essay, the author tells about visiting a place.

You can find travel essays in the travel sections of metropolitan newspapers, in travel magazines, and in the many Web sites about travel and tourism. Readers enjoy travel essays because they can find out about interesting places. And they are helped to experience the visit by seeing it through the author's eyes.

Authors of travel essays try to put the reader right there in the setting. To make the experience vivid, they may use figurative comparisons, such as simile, metaphor, and personification. As you find figurative comparisons, consider how they help you appreciate the author's viewpoint.

Organizing ideas in a figurative language chart

Notice figurative comparisons as you read, and think about why they are used.

Figurative Comparison	What Is Compared	Effects of the Comparison
Is the word *like* or *as* used? The comparison is called a simile. Is one thing said to be another? The comparison is called a metaphor. Is a nonliving thing given the traits of a person or animal? Is a nonhuman living thing given the traits of a person? The comparison is called personification.	What are the two unlike things that are being compared? How are they said to be similar?	Does the comparison suggest a mood or feeling or idea?

Keep in mind that literal comparisons are more common than figurative ones. Even though the word *like* or *as* appears in the following examples, the comparisons are literal ones and not similes: *Manuela looks like her mother. Bob is as tall as his father. The tree is as old as the house.*

Prepare for the Reading Selection

Gaining knowledge

The pages that follow contain a travel essay about a location along the coast of the state of Massachusetts. Massachusetts is in the region called New England.

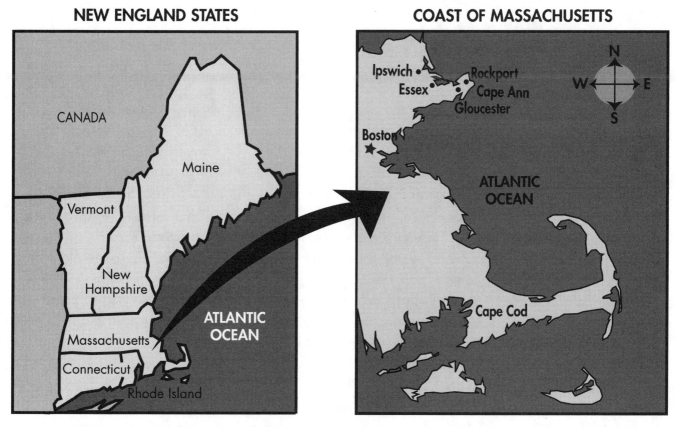

In this essay, a writer named Sarah Golland is describing her experience taking a boat cruise from a small town called Essex.

Learn Vocabulary

Understanding vocabulary

The boxed words below are **boldfaced** in the selection. Learn the meaning of each word. Then write the word beside its clue.

estuary	1. Overrun with pests _____
glaciers	2. Often called "rivers of ice" _____
debris	3. Insect-killing substance _____
infested	4. Synonym for *welcoming* _____
hospitable	5. Synonym for *soak* _____
abundant	6. Synonym for *rubble* _____
pesticide	7. Synonym for *plentiful* _____
saturate	8. Done for pleasure rather than profit _____
recreational	9. Meeting place of river and sea _____

Reading Selection—Part One

Read the first part of the travel essay "Go with the Flow" by Sarah Golland.

Go with the Flow

It is a mild day in mid-June when I, along with about thirty other passengers, climb aboard a boat for a narrated cruise along the Essex River. As we chug away from the marina, the first thing I learn is that the little Essex River is not a river at all. It is a tidal **estuary**. That means its water comes mainly from the sea and is salty. As the tide raises the sea level, water flows into the estuary, and the Essex River rises—more than eight feet at high tide, on average. Then the sea begins to call the water back. Every twelve hours, the Essex River rises and falls, responding to the slow but steady heartbeat of the tides.

This landscape, like the rest of coastal New England, is the result of events that took place ten thousand years ago. Back then, **glaciers** still covered much of northern North America. But the earth was warming, and this last ice age was ending. As the edges of the glaciers melted, the earth crawled out from under the thick frozen covers. The earth's surface showed the effects of the glacier's movement. The land had been smashed and scraped and gouged and flattened and, in some spots, raised into long, low hills called drumlins. Our captain, Dan Courtemanche, points out an island way ahead and explains that it is a drumlin, formed from piled-up rock **debris** left behind by a glacier. It is called Hog Island, so named by the English colonists, who arrived in the early 1600s, and kept their hogs on the island.

The boat meanders through passages between layered walls of dense brown soil. Green grass grows thickly on top of the soil. It is an ocean of grass, spreading far into the distance. Year after year, century after century, the grass grows and dies and decays. The soil is rich in nutrients, for it is made largely of the decaying vegetation. We are in a salt marsh.

Infested with mosquitoes, difficult to navigate, too spongy to walk or build on—salt marshes were never seen as **hospitable** places. Yet the colonists and later settlers valued these salt marshes, because salt marsh hay could be harvested and had many uses. It was nutritious and made good fodder for livestock. The tubular shape of the stalks made the hay an excellent insulator. In the early years of settlement, hay was stacked around houses to keep heat from escaping. And blocks of ice taken from frozen ponds in winter could be wrapped in salt marsh hay, and the ice would last through summer.

There is a strong connection to America's past in these small seacoast towns. Essex citizens are still proud of the working bell in their church steeple, made by none other than the famous revolutionary and silversmith Paul Revere. Essex shipyards were once famed throughout the world for the wooden vessels built for fishing and trade. The inland forests supplied the lumber—oak, locust, pine, and spruce. Once the vessels were built, it took time and ingenuity to float them down the Essex River, which was too shallow for navigation at low tide.

As Captain Courtemanche's narrative continues, we learn about the Algonkian-speaking people who fished and dug clams and set up camps in this estuary, long before the Europeans came. We pass a worn set of steps barely visible in a granite boulder. Centuries ago, native people climbed down those steps to check their fishing traps. English speakers called the people the Agawam, though that might have been a place name. Nearly all the Agawam people were wiped out by smallpox in the 1600s. The disease was spread by the English and other Europeans to Native Americans, who had no immunity to it. There are no Agawam today.

The boat glides on through the calm, dark waters.

Completing a figurative language chart   Use the figurative comparisons in the first part of the travel essay to fill out the missing sections of this chart.

Figurative Comparison	What Is Compared	Effects of the Comparison
". . . the sea begins to call the water back." (personification)		sense the motion of water and the pull of the sea
	the ocean tides and a beating heart	appreciate the regular motion of the tides and its life-giving qualities
". . . the earth crawled out from under the thick frozen covers." (personification)		
". . . an ocean of grass, . . ." (metaphor)		

Reading Selection—Part Two

Read the second part of the travel essay "Go with the Flow" by Sara Golland.

As America grew, many Atlantic salt marshes were destroyed by industrial and real-estate development. But in recent decades, more and more people have realized that tidal salt marshes are indeed hospitable—these ecosystems furnish food and habitat for countless species. The Essex River salt marsh is now recognized as a precious place and is protected by strict regulations. We are warned not to toss even a candy wrapper overboard.

great egret (Casmerodius albus)

"There's a Great Egret at two o'clock," announces Captain Courtemanche, using the image of a clock face to help us know where to look. Sure enough, just to the right of the bow, I see a white bird with a yellow bill. It is standing on long legs in the shallow water and leaning its long neck forward as gracefully as a ballet dancer. It is hunting for a fish.

Shellfish and fin fish are **abundant** in this estuary, with its constantly renewing waters, and so are the birds and animals that catch them. On top of a tall pole, we see the heavy sticks of an osprey nest. The ospreys themselves are off somewhere, and because I've seen ospreys before elsewhere, I picture them dropping from the sky to the water and rising swiftly with a fish in their strong claws. They are splendid birds of prey. Ospreys are among those top-of-the-food-chain birds that almost became extinct because of human activity, including **pesticide** use. But the nest is a triumphant announcement—at least one pair has returned to the Essex River.

Cormorants are fishing here too. These birds swim low in the water, so only their necks and heads, like submarine periscopes, are visible. They are great divers, and often disappear below the surface, to pop up far from their starting point. Cormorants lack the oil glands of other water birds, and water can **saturate** their feathers, so the birds must dry out in the air. They stand on rocks, slightly hunched, and hold out their wings like a black cape. They could be extras in a Dracula movie.

double-crested cormorant (Phalacrocorax auritus)

The estuary feeds people, too. Long ago, there were so many lobsters here that people had only to walk along the beach to collect them. Lobsters were the main food of the servants and other commonfolk. Too many were collected too fast, however, which is why lobsters are now a costly treat. There are not enough lobsters in the estuary to sustain an industry, though licenses are issued for **recreational** trapping. Colored buoys bob in the water, marking the lobster traps below. Seals know to look for lobster traps here, and they sometimes take the lobsters for themselves. I scan the glittering surface for seals, but don't see any today.

The mud flats hold lots of other shellfish, including blue mussels, quahogs, and the soft-shell clams that bring crowds of tourists to the Essex clam shacks. Clamming has always been a human activity here, and is still a major industry.

The yellow-gold ribbons stretching ahead of us are the sands of the beautiful barrier beaches, and beyond them is the open ocean. This is where the Essex River ends, and it is time to turn back. On the return trip, Captain Courtemanche continues telling us about the estuary—its people, its wildlife, its past. Like cruise narrators everywhere, he makes the occasional corny joke, but nobody groans or scoffs. I smile, because it is impossible not to. The breeze feels warm and friendly. The air, with just a touch of salt, tastes fresh. Out here on the water, it is as restful as a quiet song.

Wherever land meets sea, interesting things happen. In this tiny estuary, barely visible on a map of New England, there is so much to experience. I think I'll come back.

Using a figurative language chart

Find examples of simile, metaphor, and personification in the second part of the travel essay. Fill out this chart with your findings and ideas.

Figurative Comparison	What Is Compared	Effects of the Comparison

Check Your Understanding

Think about what you've read. Then answer these questions.

1. When describing the last ice age, the author says that "the earth crawled out from under the thick frozen covers." What are the "thick frozen covers"?
   - Ⓐ a quilt or other bedding
   - Ⓑ glaciers
   - Ⓒ rocks and soil
   - Ⓓ the icy ocean

2. The osprey nest is compared to an "announcement." What is a likely announcement, based on information in the essay?
   - Ⓐ "Our babies have arrived!"
   - Ⓑ "Watch us drop from the sky!"
   - Ⓒ "We are at the top of the food chain."
   - Ⓓ "We have survived!"

3. What is a main difference between a river and a tidal estuary?
   - Ⓐ A tidal estuary does not have much fresh water.
   - Ⓑ A tidal estuary meets the sea.
   - Ⓒ A river is narrow.
   - Ⓓ A tidal estuary provides habitat for many birds.

4. Why are salt marshes considered hospitable places?
   - Ⓐ People can build homes in them.
   - Ⓑ Illness can be cured in them.
   - Ⓒ Living things thrive in them.
   - Ⓓ They have mosquitoes, are hard to navigate, and are spongy to walk on.

5. What is abundant in the Essex River today?
   - Ⓐ wooden vessels
   - Ⓑ pollution
   - Ⓒ ospreys
   - Ⓓ clams

6. Salt marsh hay is an excellent insulator. That is why people of the past used it to
   - Ⓐ build boats.
   - Ⓑ feed animals.
   - Ⓒ wrap ice for storage.
   - Ⓓ build their houses.

7. The author sees worn steps in a granite boulder. The steps were made by
   - Ⓐ boat builders.
   - Ⓑ glaciers.
   - Ⓒ English colonists.
   - Ⓓ Native Americans.

8. Why does the author use words such as *meander* and *glide* to describe the action of the boat?
   - Ⓐ to help readers feel the rising tide under the boat
   - Ⓑ to convey the restful, gentle mood of the setting
   - Ⓒ to show how interesting the experience was
   - Ⓓ to explain how the boat motor works

9. Why are lobsters more costly now than in the past?
   - Ⓐ Wealthy people like eating them now.
   - Ⓑ Lobsters are less abundant now.
   - Ⓒ There is more recreational trapping now.
   - Ⓓ In the past, poor people ate them.

10. Which of these statements from the travel essay includes an opinion?
    - Ⓐ It is a mild day in mid-June. . . .
    - Ⓑ Green grass grows thickly on top of the soil.
    - Ⓒ They are splendid birds of prey.
    - Ⓓ Clamming has always been a human activity here. . . .

11. Nobody scoffs at the captain's corny jokes. Why might the author have mentioned that?
    A to show that everyone is feeling tolerant and in good humor
    B so that the reader can imagine the eye-rolling and groaning
    C to show that everybody is paying attention to the scenery, not to the captain
    D so that the reader can understand the jokes

12. The title of this travel essay is a fitting one because it suggests
    A a pleasant feeling of ease.
    B gentle ocean breezes.
    C the connection between past and present.
    D a cruise on a tidal estuary.

Extend Your Learning

- *A Familiar Place*

  Visit a familiar spot, but try to see it with fresh eyes. Write at least one paragraph about what you see, hear, and feel. Use figurative language that helps your readers experience the place as you do.

- *Dream Destinations*

  What coastal regions might the members of your group like to visit some day? Start by using a globe or map to choose several locations. Then use print and on-line sources to zoom in on each choice, until you find a particular site or tour that intrigues you. Write an advertisement for each destination, using language that appeals to the senses.

- *Vivid Settings*

  Find a written work that has vivid descriptions of a setting. Examples are a travel essay, a nonfiction article about a place, a short story or novel in which the setting is important. As you read, notice any figurative comparisons. After reading, go back to make a figurative language chart that helps you analyze and appreciate the author's choice of words.

Summarizing

Learn About Summarizing

Thinking about the strategy

A **summary** is a shortened version of a story, an article, or any other work of fiction or nonfiction. In order to make a summary, readers must review the text, reflect on the most important information, and put it into their own words. Because summarizing requires careful, focused thinking about a text, it is a useful reading and study strategy.

To write a summary of nonfiction, try to answer the question, *What is the work mainly about?* Separate the main ideas of passages from the supporting details, and include the main ideas in your summary. The length of your summary depends on your purpose, but it should always be much shorter than the original.

A summary of fiction usually identifies story elements. The setting is where and when the story takes place. The main character faces a problem or wants to reach a goal. Minor characters may help, or hinder, the main character. The plot is the action of the story—what happens. The theme of the story is the "big idea" that you find in it. (Not all stories have a theme.) A theme is larger than the story itself, and might be an idea about honesty, heroism, or persistence, for example.

Studying a model

Read this legend and the notes beside it.

<u>Setting</u>: 14th century Switzerland

<u>Main character</u>: William Tell

<u>Minor characters</u>: Austrian governor Gessler, Tell's young son

<u>Plot</u>: Gessler commands Swiss to bow to his cap on top of pole.

William Tell refuses to bow and is arrested.

Tell is forced to shoot an apple off his son's head.

He succeeds, but reveals that Gessler would have been shot had the boy been hurt.

Tell goes on to lead revolt and become national legendary hero of Switzerland.

<u>Theme</u>: It takes a hero to challenge tyranny.

In the 1300s, Austrian overlords ruled the Swiss people. An Austrian governor named Gessler was especially tyrannical. Gessler erected a tall pole in a public square and placed his cap on top of it. His soldiers stood in the square to make sure that everyone who passed bowed to Gessler's cap.

William Tell was a proud and brave Swiss hunter, known as a fine marksman with his crossbow. In the public square one day, he passed by the tall pole with Gessler's cap. Instead of bowing, Tell merely sneered. The soldiers arrested him.

"Anyone who dares to defy my orders must be taught a lesson," said Gessler when William Tell was brought before him. "You claim to be a marksman. You will make a public demonstration of your skill. You must shoot an apple off the head of your son. If you succeed, I will free you. If you fail, you will be executed."

An apple was placed on the head of William Tell's young son. The boy stood perfectly still, trusting in his father. William Tell lifted his bow, aimed, and released the arrow. It flew to the center of the apple and split it in half. The crowd cheered.

As William Tell ran to embrace his son, another arrow fell from his shirt. "Why do you have a second arrow?" asked Gessler. "You were allowed one."

"If I had hurt my son," William Tell said to Gessler, "the arrow was for you."

William Tell soon led the Swiss revolt against the Austrian oppressors. He is the legendary national hero of Switzerland.

Learn About a Graphic Organizer

Understanding a story map

To organize ideas for a summary of a fictional work, make a **story map**.
A story map shows the story elements and their connections to one another.

This story map shows story elements from the legend of William Tell on page 114.

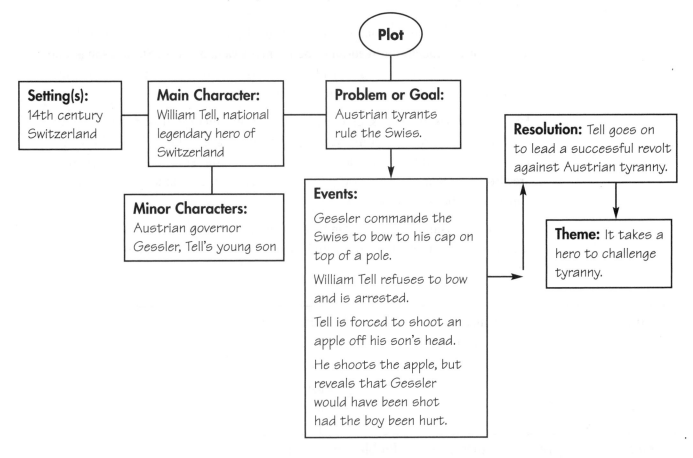

Plot

Setting(s): 14th century Switzerland

Main Character: William Tell, national legendary hero of Switzerland

Minor Characters: Austrian governor Gessler, Tell's young son

Problem or Goal: Austrian tyrants rule the Swiss.

Events:

Gessler commands the Swiss to bow to his cap on top of a pole.

William Tell refuses to bow and is arrested.

Tell is forced to shoot an apple off his son's head.

He shoots the apple, but reveals that Gessler would have been shot had the boy been hurt.

Resolution: Tell goes on to lead a successful revolt against Austrian tyranny.

Theme: It takes a hero to challenge tyranny.

You can use the story map information to write a summary of the legend.
This example summary is about one third the length of the original.

> William Tell is the national legendary hero of Switzerland. His leadership in the fourteenth century helped bring about the end of tyrannical Austrian rule. According to legend, when William Tell refused to bow to the cap that the Austrian governor, Gessler, had placed on top of a pole, Tell was forced to shoot an apple off the head of his own son. He shot successfully, but revealed that his second arrow would have been used on Gessler had the boy been harmed.

As you read, ask yourself

- What are the story elements?
- How can I sum up the most important events?

Learn About a Form of Writing

Focusing on a legend

A **legend** is a form of traditional folklore. Like all traditional tales, legends were first told orally. Legends may overlap with other forms of folklore, such as myths or tall tales, but the usual distinguishing feature of a legend is its origin. A legend is often based on real events.

A legend may feature a heroic person who really lived—someone who founded a nation, for example, or fought for freedom or performed a valiant rescue. Stories, songs, and poems are told about the person, and as the years pass, the stories veer farther and farther from the facts. They turn into legends.

Every culture has its legends. Legendary figures from American history include Johnny Appleseed, who loved freedom and apple trees; the brave and wild backwoodsman Davy Crockett; and the powerful, determined tunnel builder John Henry. Legends are also told about settings—how particular rock formations came to be, or where a mysterious buried treasure lies.

The written versions of legends can be read purely for entertainment. But thoughtful readers may find more; they may gain insight into the values and the history of the culture of origin.

Organizing ideas in a story map

A story map like this one can help you focus on story elements and prepare a written summary.

Plot

Setting(s): Where and when do events take place?

Main Character: Who is the legendary hero? What is the hero like?

Minor Characters: What enemies does the hero have? Who helps the hero?

Problem or Goal: Why does the hero have a problem? What must the hero do?

Events: What are the most important things that happen as the hero tries to solve the problem?

Resolution: What happens at the end?

Theme: What big idea or lesson, if any, can you find in the legend?

Prepare for the Reading Selection

Gaining knowledge

The pages that follow contain a retelling of a legend about a Chinese hero, a man known as Chu-ko Liang (also called Kung Ming). Chu-ko Liang lived from A.D. 181 to 234, and played an important role in the attempt to reunify China.

Chu-ko Liang was known as a skillful leader with remarkable military judgment. It was said that he could predict the future. If he did indeed make successful predictions, it was likely that they were based on his broad scientific knowledge. Chu-ko Liang was also a respected poet.

Singers and storytellers praised Chu-ko Liang. His fame spread even more widely after his exploits appeared in a popular fourteenth-century work of historical fiction. Chu-ko Liang had achieved legendary status.

Learn Vocabulary

Understanding vocabulary

The boxed words below are **boldfaced** in the selection. Learn the meaning of each word. Then write the word beside its clue.

| alliance |
| strategist |
| suspicion |
| skeptically |
| sympathetic |
| indistinguishable |
| ambush |
| visibility |
| embedded |
| reluctantly |

1. This can describe a black cat on a moonless night. _____

2. Something formed in friendship. _____

3. Clues to a crime may cause this. _____

4. The opposite of a formal battle. _____

5. How you do something you don't want to do. _____

6. An eyebrow may be raised this way. _____

7. A friend can offer this kind of listening. _____

8. A name for a skillful military planner. _____

9. A synonym for *stuck*. _____

10. When this is good, you can see clearly. _____

Read the first part of the legend "The Borrowed Arrows."

The Borrowed Arrows

Eighteen centuries ago, China was divided into warring kingdoms. The most powerful of the kingdoms was Wei, which was ruled by Tsao Tsao.

The two lesser kingdoms of Wu and Shu formed an **alliance** because their leaders knew they would have a better chance of beating back Tsao Tsao's armies if they combined their forces. There was a big problem, however. The Shu ruler, Chou Yu, was commander-in-chief and thus had authority over the Wu general, Chu-ko Liang. Chou Yu despised Chu-ko Liang. His reason? Chu-ko Liang was such a brilliant military **strategist** that he outshone his commander. Chu-ko Liang was also widely respected as a man of learning and of deep understanding of human nature. Despite their shared enemy, Chou Yu wanted nothing more than to see Chu-ko Liang fail. But Chou Yu could not think of a way to get rid of his so-called ally without arousing **suspicion**.

Tsao Tsao's troops were encamped on one bank of the Yangtze River. Many miles downstream, the allies' troops were on the other bank. One morning, Chu-ko Liang was ordered to come to Chou Yu's headquarters for a strategy meeting. "I plan to send our warships upstream to do battle," said Chou Yu. "What weapons should we use?"

"I think arrows would be best," replied Chu-ko Liang.

"I think so too," said Chou Yu quickly. "I have determined that our troops will require one hundred thousand arrows. I am putting you in charge of producing the arrows."

"I will do what you wish," said Chu-ko Liang with an obedient bow. "By what date do you want these arrows?"

"Ten days from now," answered Chou Yu.

Chu-ko Liang calculated silently. "I think ten days is too long to wait," he said.

"When do you propose?"

"I believe it would be best to do battle in three days."

"Do you really think you can deliver one hundred thousand arrows in just three days?" asked Chou Yu **skeptically**.

"Yes," said Chu-ko Liang.

"Surely you are mistaken."

"I would not say it if I did not think I could do it," said Chu-ko Liang. "If you do not believe me, just make it a command. If I cannot fulfill your command, you may set whatever punishment you wish."

Chou Yu's pulse quickened. An honest opportunity to punish his rival had just been delivered to him! Chou Yu glanced around the tent to make sure that other officers had heard the exchange. Then he said to Chu-ko Liang, "I hereby order you to deliver one hundred thousand arrows in three days' time."

Chu-ko Liang said, "On the morning of the day after the day after tomorrow, send ships to my camp to collect the arrows." He bowed, then left.

Chou Yu immediately sent secret orders to the suppliers of bamboo, feathers, glue, and other arrow-making materials. They were told to reply to requests from Chu-ko Liang by saying that these products were out of stock.

That evening, Chou Yu told Lu Su, one of his generals, to go to Chu-ko Liang's tent. "Learn what you can about his plans," said Chou Yu.

This was not the first time Lu Su had been sent to spy on Chu-ko Liang. Lu Su always played the part of a **sympathetic** friend.

"Welcome, General Lu," said Chu-ko Liang. "I was expecting you. Please join me for dinner."

As Lu Su was enjoying the meal, Chu-ko Liang said, "The Shu commander has decided to prevent me from making the arrows. He has told the suppliers that my arrow makers are not to be furnished with the necessary materials."

"I cannot believe it!" said Lu Su, although he knew it was true.

Completing a story map   Refer to the first part of "The Borrowed Arrows" to add to the information in this story map. Leave room in the "Events" frame to add more items after reading the second part. Leave the "Resolution" and "Theme" frames blank for now.

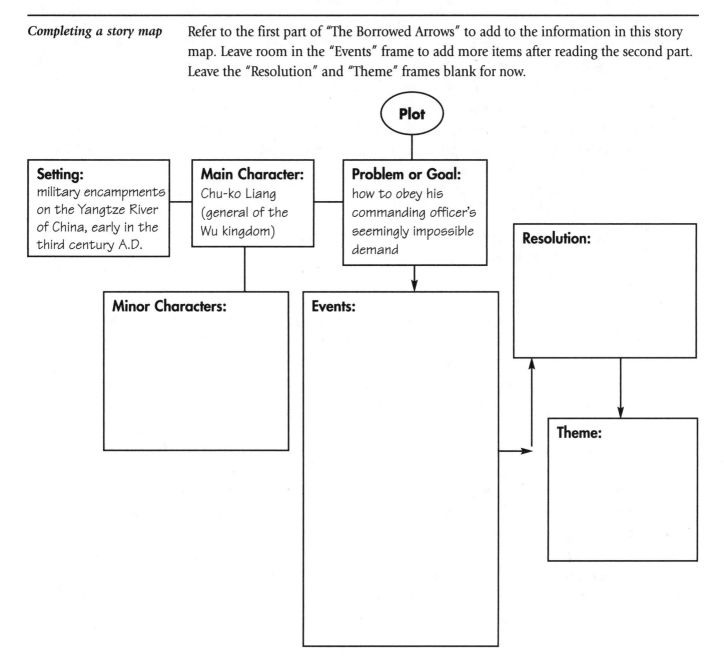

(**Plot**)

Setting:
military encampments on the Yangtze River of China, early in the third century A.D.

Main Character:
Chu-ko Liang (general of the Wu kingdom)

Problem or Goal:
how to obey his commanding officer's seemingly impossible demand

Minor Characters:

Events:

Resolution:

Theme:

Read the second part of the legend "The Borrowed Arrows."

"Please remember why our forces have joined," said Chu-ko Liang to Lu Su. "We have a common enemy. Let us work together to defeat him." Chu-ko Liang's eyes were gentle, his manner mild.

"I would help you if I could," said Lu Su.

"I was hoping you would say that," said Chu-ko Liang. "You can help me. Please lend me twenty small boats, each with thirty men. Every boat must be filled with bundles of straw."

"Surely you do not expect to challenge the great navy of Tsao Tsao with twenty small boats!" said Lu Su.

"It warms my heart to see your concern, my friend," said Chu-ko Liang. "But do not worry. Do you agree to provide me with the straw, the vessels, and the crews?"

"Yes," said Lu Su. "I can send them by tomorrow afternoon."

"Fine, fine," said Chu-ko Liang. "And you are welcome to join me here at sunset on the day after. That will be just before the third day—when I will have to fulfill my promise to produce the arrows."

Lu Su had the boats delivered. Early the following evening, Lu Su found Chu-ko Liang giving orders to officers assembled on the river bank. Twenty small boats were joined stern to bow with rope. Each boat in the line was packed with bales of straw. Bales were also lashed to the sides.

Just after sunset, the air began to fill with mist. Soon it turned into a thick, blinding fog that enveloped everyone and everything. The water was **indistinguishable** from the land. The boats looked like shapeless shadows, bulging with strange forms.

"Come aboard with me," Chu-ko Liang said to Lu Su, gesturing toward the cabin of one of the boats. The two men settled into the cabin.

The crew of thirty began rowing upstream. Nineteen other crews rowed in the other boats. "Where are we going?" asked Lu Su.

"To get our arrows," said Chu-ko Liang. "Or, more precisely, to *borrow* our arrows."

"Borrow?" asked Lu Su. "From whom?"

"From our enemy, Tsao Tsao," said Chu-ko Liang. Lu Su's jaw dropped, but he said nothing.

After several hours, an officer entered to tell Chu-ko Liang that they had arrived at their destination. "Give the signal," ordered Chu-ko Liang.

Not long after, a great gong sounded, drums rolled, and the sailors in the twenty little boats shouted and roared as fiercely as ten thousand men.

"Are we attacking?" cried Lu Su.

"No," replied Chu-ko Liang. "We're only pretending to attack. The men are safe below deck. Tsao Tsao's forces cannot see us through this thick fog. They will try to stop us, though."

On the banks of the Yangtze, Tsao Tsao's commanders strained to see through the dense fog. A large naval force seemed to be out there, about to **ambush** them. The Wei commanders decided against launching warships when **visibility** was this poor. Instead, they ordered their land-based archers to shoot at the floating shapes.

Each boat bobbed and shuddered as arrows by the hundreds rained down and **embedded** themselves in the bales of straw. Then the gong sounded again, followed by more drumming and loud shouting. That was the signal for the boats to turn, enabling arrows to fill the bales on the other side.

As dawn approached, the fog began to lift. Chu-ko Liang gave the order to row downstream. Speedily, the twenty boats, bristling with arrows, headed downstream to Chu-ko Liang's encampment.

"Look at all these arrows!" said Lu Su with amazement.

"I would guess there are at least one hundred thousand," said Chu-ko Liang. "We will deliver them to Chou Yu. Then he can decide when to return them to Tsao Tsao."

"But how did you know?" asked Lu Su.

"Know what?"

"Know that there would be a fog?" asked Lu Su.

"I read the weather signs three days ago," said Chu-ko Liang. "I knew when the fog would arrive, so I knew when I had to make the voyage upstream."

"But how did you know you would have to make the voyage?"

"Oh, that," said Chu-ko Liang with a smile. "I sensed that I might have to borrow arrows rather than make them myself."

By noon of the third day, Commander-in-Chief Chou had his hundred thousand arrows. He announced that Chu-ko Liang had obeyed his commander and fulfilled his duty. **Reluctantly**, he admitted that Chu-ko Liang had shone brilliantly once again.

Using a story map

Turn back to page 119 to complete the story map for "The Borrowed Arrows." Refer to the map in order to write a one-paragraph summary of the legend. Write on the lines below.

_____

_____

_____

_____

_____

_____

_____

_____

_____

_____

_____

_____

Check Your Understanding

Think about what you've read. Then answer these questions.

1. What was Chou Yu's goal?
   - Ⓐ to borrow 100,000 arrows
   - Ⓑ to get rid of Chu-ko Liang
   - Ⓒ to defend himself from Chu-ko Liang
   - Ⓓ to take over the kingdom of Shu

2. Which minor character helps the main character?
   - Ⓐ Tsao Tsao
   - Ⓑ Chou Yu
   - Ⓒ Lu Su
   - Ⓓ Chu-ko Liang

3. What is the purpose of the alliance between Wu and Shu?
   - Ⓐ to fight a common enemy
   - Ⓑ to combine their armies with that of Wei
   - Ⓒ to help Tsao Tsao
   - Ⓓ to establish the rules of war between them

4. The main talent of a strong military strategist is the ability to
   - Ⓐ predict the weather.
   - Ⓑ predict the actions of other military commanders.
   - Ⓒ seem to be telling the truth while lying.
   - Ⓓ keep plans secret.

5. Chou Yu reacts skeptically to the offer to have the arrows delivered in three days. What does *skeptically* mean?
   - Ⓐ "with doubt"
   - Ⓑ "as if secretly thrilled"
   - Ⓒ "mournfully"
   - Ⓓ "instantly"

6. Why does Chu-ko Liang prefer to deliver the arrows in three days, rather than in ten?
   - Ⓐ to demonstrate his obedience to Chou Yu
   - Ⓑ to allow the battle to take place at the best possible time
   - Ⓒ to take advantage of the fog he knows is coming
   - Ⓓ to show that his plan is superior to Chou Yu's

7. Which of these is Chu-ko Liang's most likely action immediately after he leaves Chou Yu's headquarters?
   - Ⓐ try unsuccessfully to order the materials for making arrows
   - Ⓑ make a weather prediction
   - Ⓒ order his troops to pack hay on twenty small boats
   - Ⓓ make a plan for persuading Lu Su to help

8. Why are the bales of hay packed onto the twenty vessels?
   - Ⓐ to feed animals
   - Ⓑ to hold the points of arrows
   - Ⓒ to hide sailors
   - Ⓓ to make the vessels look like giant warships

9. What do Chu-ko Liang's sailors do off the shore of the Wei encampment?
   - Ⓐ yell like attacking warriors
   - Ⓑ shoot arrows by the thousands
   - Ⓒ ambush Tsao Tsao's troops
   - Ⓓ hide quietly

10. Why aren't Chu-ko Liang's little boats attacked by enemy warships?
    - Ⓐ The enemy is nowhere to be found.
    - Ⓑ The enemy commanders see that they are outnumbered.
    - Ⓒ The enemy recognizes that the boats are too small to cause harm.
    - Ⓓ The enemy does not want to launch warships in the fog.

11. Why are the arrows described as "borrowed"?

Ⓐ Chou Yu will shoot them back at the enemy.

Ⓑ Tsao Tsao's navy will try to get them back.

Ⓒ They belong to nobody.

Ⓓ They have not been paid for.

12. This legend reveals that in ancient China, the people valued

Ⓐ peace above all else.

Ⓑ cleverness.

Ⓒ freedom to make personal choices.

Ⓓ weaponry.

Extend Your Learning

- *Write a Skit*

  Retell the legend "The Borrowed Arrows" in play form. Write a skit featuring the three characters Chu-ko Liang, Chou Yu, and Lu Su. Challenge yourself to show the plot through the characters' dialogue and gestures alone. Have the characters reveal their traits and motives through what they say and how they say it.

- *Research Local Legends*

  With your group, use resources such as the local historical society, the library catalog, and Internet search engines to learn about legendary figures and sites in your town, city, or region. Create retellings and "Fact or Fiction" items. Consider publishing your findings in a tourist brochure or on an educational Web site.

- *Read a Legend*

  Read another legend about a heroic figure from any culture. Robin Hood and King Arthur are just two possibilities, both from English history. Make a story map to organize the story elements, and summarize the legend in just one or two paragraphs.

Reading Selection One

Read the excerpt from an interview with the well-known marine biologist Sylvia Earle.

What's your most important contribution to understanding marine life?

I've had the great pleasure of finding new kinds of plants and animals, of being the first in certain places under the ocean. All that's very rewarding. But if I can accomplish one thing, it will be to inspire others to see for themselves and not feel that this is off-limits. The ocean is here for all of us.

Have people stopped dumping poison in the seas?

There have been some encouraging new guidelines to inhibit the deliberate dumping of things of a noxious sort, nationally and internationally. But the ocean is the ultimate sewer for human society—what we put into the atmosphere falls back, often as polluted substances like acid rain. What we put on our lawns, golf courses, fields, and farms flows through groundwater into rivers and, ultimately, the ocean.

How good are the current data on fish populations?

It doesn't take a scientist dripping with degrees to give the broad assessment that the oceans are in trouble. It's partly what we are putting into the ocean. It's also what we're deliberately removing, through the most incredible techniques for extracting wild animals from ecosystems that have ever been devised. We are new predators on ecosystems that have been tens of millions, hundreds of millions of years in the making.

Do you eat seafood?

I was raised on it, but I now know too much to enjoy eating it anymore, so I do abstain. I feel like if I could go around passing out face masks and flippers, like Johnny Flipperseed or something, to get people to go jump in the ocean and see for themselves what it's like, we would go a long way toward bridging the gap that currently causes us to consume fish as if they're infinitely abundant.

What's the deepest that you've dived?

Well, part of what motivates me to speak for the fish, if you will, is that I have seen them on their own terms, in circumstances other than swimming with lemon slices in butter. I've seen them at depths of over 13,000 feet.

What have you learned at such depths?

In deep water as well as shallow, that the ocean is alive—it's not just rocks and water out there, but a living minestrone, top to bottom. It shapes the chemistry of the planet, the character of our life-support system. Life in the ocean gives rise to 70 percent of the oxygen that sustains us.

You've said you're a scientist above all, before being a woman and a mother.

Yes. A scientist is a child in a different package, with the same kind of wonder and inquisitiveness—I just never lost it. Kids always have it, and most scientists continue to have it. It's a kind of detachment, but also an intense involvement in what you're doing and a profound sense of wanting to know what's there or how things behave. Every day, you know a little bit more, and it puts you in a position to ask better questions.

Check Your Understanding

Think about what you've read. Then answer these questions.

1. What does Sylvia Earle say is more important than being the first to explore certain areas of ocean?
   Ⓐ finding new kinds of plants and animals
   Ⓑ guaranteeing that parts of the ocean remain off-limits
   Ⓒ understanding marine life
   Ⓓ getting other people to appreciate the ocean

2. When Earle calls the ocean "the ultimate sewer," what main point is she making?
   Ⓐ The ocean receives all the waste products of human activity.
   Ⓑ The ocean is too unhealthy for living things.
   Ⓒ The ocean has the capacity to carry away pollution.
   Ⓓ People have made it illegal to dump poisons in the ocean.

3. The interviewer asks, "How good are the current data on fish populations?" What do the current data probably show?
   Ⓐ Fish numbers are dropping.
   Ⓑ More research is needed.
   Ⓒ Fish live in large groups.
   Ⓓ Fish populations are growing.

4. Sylvia Earle says we now have "the most incredible techniques for extracting wild animals from ecosystems that have ever been devised."
   How does she feel about those techniques?
   Ⓐ enthusiastic
   Ⓑ fearful
   Ⓒ somewhat hopeful
   Ⓓ astonished

5. According to Earle, if people could just jump in the ocean and explore it as she has, they would
   Ⓐ see that the oceans are in trouble.
   Ⓑ see the infinite abundance of life.
   Ⓒ eat less fish.
   Ⓓ wear face masks and flippers.

6. Earle compares the ocean to a minestrone, which is a soup known for its
   Ⓐ spicy flavors.
   Ⓑ varied ingredients.
   Ⓒ simplicity.
   Ⓓ thickness.

7. Which of these statements includes an opinion?
   Ⓐ "I've seen them at depths of over 13,000 feet."
   Ⓑ "There have been some encouraging new guidelines to inhibit the deliberate dumping of things of a noxious sort. . . ."
   Ⓒ "What we put on our lawns, golf courses, fields, and farms flows through groundwater into rivers and, ultimately, the ocean."
   Ⓓ "Life in the ocean gives rise to 70 percent of the oxygen that sustains us."

8. Why does Sylvia Earle say that she has seen fish at depths of over 13,000 feet?
   Ⓐ to describe the deep ocean
   Ⓑ to point out that she has had unusual experiences
   Ⓒ to support her idea that fish are abundant
   Ⓓ to explain that the entire ocean has life

9. In her answer to the last question, Sylvia Earle uses the word *detachment*. What is detachment?
   Ⓐ intense involvement
   Ⓑ curiosity
   Ⓒ lack of opinion or bias
   Ⓓ confidence

10. Which of these statements belongs in a summary of this interview?
    Ⓐ Sylvia Earle has the wonder and inquisitiveness of a child.
    Ⓑ Sylvia Earle believes that the ocean is here for everyone to protect and enjoy.
    Ⓒ Sylvia Earle knows too much about ocean life to enjoy eating seafood now.
    Ⓓ Sylvia Earle has discovered new kinds of plants and animals in the ocean.

Reading Selection Two

Read the folktale from Italy.

Crab the Peasant

There was once a king who had lost a valuable ring. He looked for it everywhere, but could not find it. So he issued a proclamation that any astrologer who could tell him where it was would be richly rewarded. A poor peasant by the name of Crab heard of the proclamation. Like most peasants, he could neither read nor write, but he took it into his head that he wanted to be the astrologer to the king.

So the peasant went and presented himself to the king, and said, "Your Majesty, although I am poorly dressed, I am indeed an astrologer. I know that you have lost a ring, and I will try by study to see where it is."

"Very well," said the king. "Go, then, study, and we shall see what kind of astrologer you turn out to be."

Crab was conducted to a room, in which he was shut up to study. It contained only a bed and a table on which were a large book and writing materials. He seated himself at the table. Since he knew nothing of reading or writing, he busied himself turning the leaves of the book and scribbling on the paper so that the servants who brought him his food thought him a wise and great man. The servants were the thieves who had stolen the ring, and from the severe glances that Crab cast at them whenever they entered, they began to fear that they would be found out. They made him endless bows and never opened their mouths without calling him "Mr. Astrologer." Crab may have been illiterate, but he was as cunning as any peasant, and at once imagined that the servants must know about the ring. He decided to confirm his suspicions.

He had been shut up in his room turning over his big book and scribbling his paper for a month, when his wife came to visit him. He said to her, "Hide yourself under the bed, and when a servant enters, say, 'That is one'; when another comes, say, 'That is two' and so on."

The woman hid herself. The servants came with dinner, and hardly had the first one entered when a voice from under the bed said, "That is one." The second servant entered, and the voice said, "That is two," and so on. The servants were frightened at hearing that voice, for they did not know where it came from.

126

They held a consultation, and one of them said, "We are discovered; if the astrologer denounces us to the king as thieves, we are lost."

Another said, "We must go to the astrologer and tell him frankly that we stole the ring, and ask him not to betray us, and present him with a purse of money. Are you willing?"

"Perfectly," the other servants said together.

So the servants went in harmony to the astrologer, and making him a lower bow than usual, one of them began, "Mr. Astrologer, sir, you have discovered that we stole the ring. We are poor people and if you reveal it to the king, we are undone. So we beg you not to betray us, and accept this purse of money."

Crab took the money and said, "I will not betray you, but you must do what I tell you, if you wish to save your lives. Take the ring and make that turkey in the courtyard swallow it, and leave the rest to me."

The servants departed with a low bow. The next day Crab went to the king and said, "Your Majesty, after having toiled over a month I have succeeded in discovering where the ring has gone to."

"Where is it, then?" asked the king.

"A turkey has swallowed it."

"A turkey? Very well, let us see."

So they went for the turkey, opened it, and found the ring inside. The king, amazed, presented the astrologer with a large purse of money and invited him to a banquet.

Now, at the banquet, among the other dishes there was brought on the table a plate of crabs. Crabs must then have been very rare, because only the king and a few others knew what they were.

Turning to the peasant, the king said, "You, who are an astrologer, must be able to tell me the name of these things which are in this dish."

The poor astrologer was very much puzzled, and, as if speaking to himself, but in such a way that the others heard him, he muttered, "Ah! Crab, Crab, what a plight you are in!"

Then all, who did not know that his name was Crab, rose and proclaimed him the greatest astrologer in the world.

Check Your Understanding

Think about what you've read. Then answer these questions.

11. How can you tell this is a folktale and not another form of fiction?
    Ⓐ The setting is long ago.
    Ⓑ A problem sets the plot in motion.
    Ⓒ The overall tone is humorous.
    Ⓓ Characters are easily fooled.

12. At the time this folktale was first told, astrologers were probably
    Ⓐ scientific thinkers.   Ⓒ advisers.
    Ⓑ astronomers.   Ⓓ peasants.

13. Crab "busied himself turning the leaves of the book and scribbling on the paper. . . ." Why?
    Ⓐ to pretend to be wise and learned
    Ⓑ to find the king's lost ring
    Ⓒ to study astrology
    Ⓓ to try to learn to read and write

14. What effect do Crab's "severe glances" have on the servants?
    Ⓐ They become fearful.
    Ⓑ They steal the ring.
    Ⓒ They decide to confess.
    Ⓓ They realize he is a phony astrologer.

15. Which of these events happens first?
    Ⓐ The first servant hears a strange voice saying, "That is one."
    Ⓑ Crab's wife hides under the bed.
    Ⓒ Crab confirms his suspicions about the servants.
    Ⓓ The servants make a turkey swallow the ring.

16. Which of these details helps you predict that Crab will figure out what has happened to the king's ring?
    Ⓐ Crab takes "it into his head that he wanted to be the astrologer to the king."
    Ⓑ The king says, "we shall see what kind of astrologer you turn out to be."
    Ⓒ Crab is "as cunning as any peasant."
    Ⓓ Crab tells the king, "A turkey has swallowed it."

17. When does Crab receive a second purse of money?
    Ⓐ when he accepts a bribe from the servants
    Ⓑ when he accepts the king's challenge to study alone in a room
    Ⓒ when he agrees not to betray the servants
    Ⓓ when he shows the king that he has found the ring

18. When the servants tell Crab that they will be "undone," they mean that they will be
    Ⓐ poor.
    Ⓑ punished.
    Ⓒ guilty.
    Ⓓ revealed.

19. Which of these statements belongs in a summary of this folktale?
    Ⓐ Crab is proclaimed the greatest astrologer in the world.
    Ⓑ Crab somehow knows that the rare things in the plate are called crabs.
    Ⓒ The king is amazed that someone who cannot read nor write can solve puzzles so cleverly.
    Ⓓ The king says, "You, who are an astrologer, must be able to tell me the name of these things which are in this dish."

20. What is the most likely reason this folktale was told?
    Ⓐ to describe palace life for listeners who could never see it for themselves
    Ⓑ to entertain listeners with a ridiculous series of events
    Ⓒ to get listeners involved in the life of a main character like themselves
    Ⓓ to teach listeners the value of learning